*Houghton Mifflin*
# Mathematics

W9-CSZ-983

# Practice
# Masters

Number of Butterflies Seen

3 in.

**3**

## HOUGHTON MIFFLIN

BOSTON • MORRIS PLAINS, NJ

California • Colorado • Georgia • Illinois • New Jersey • Texas

# Contents

Name _____     Date _____

# Numbers Through 999

**Example**

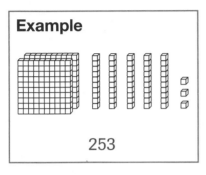

253

Write each number in standard form.

**1.**

_____

**2.**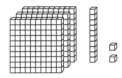

_____

**3.** 4 hundreds 6 tens 8 ones

_____

**4.** 7 hundreds 4 tens 2 ones

_____

**5.** 800 + 20 + 7

_____

**6.** 100 + 30 + 9

_____

**7.** 300 + 90

_____

Write the place of the underlined digit. Then write its value.

**8.** 7̲16

_____

**9.** 9<u>3</u>8

_____

**10.** 59<u>0</u>

_____

**11.** <u>3</u>56

_____

## Problem Solving • Reasoning

**12.** The Cleveland Metroparks Zoo has five hundred ninety-nine species of animals. What is the number of species written in standard form?

_____

**13.** The Denver Zoo has six hundred seventy-two species of animals. What is the number of species at the Denver Zoo written in expanded form?

_____

Name _____    Date _____

# Round Two-Digit Numbers

| Example |
|---------|
| 62 |
| 60 and 70 |

**Write the two tens each number is between.**

**1.** 56

_____

**2.** 25

_____

**3.** 87

_____

**4.** 64

_____

**5.** 33

_____

**Round each amount to the nearest ten or ten cents.**

**6.** 62

_____

**7.** 64¢

_____

**8.** 68¢

_____

**9.** 65

_____

**10.** 61¢

_____

**11.** 67

_____

## Problem Solving

**12.** Kyle went on a weekend ride of about 20 miles with his horseback riding club. If the actual distance was rounded to the nearest ten, which of these distances could Kyle have ridden: 14 miles, 22 miles, or 28 miles?

_____

**13.** Sophia trained for a race with her running club. She ran about 50 miles during one week. If the actual distance was rounded to the nearest ten. Which of these distances could she have run: 44 miles, 48 miles, or 56 miles?

_____

Name _____    Date _____

# Round Three-Digit Numbers

| Example |
| --- |
| 525 |
| 500 and 600 |

**Write the two hundreds each number is between.**

**1.** 342

**2.** 184

_____    _____

**Tell which two tens each number is between.**

**3.** 333

**4.** 394

**5.** 502

_____    _____    _____

**Round to the nearest hundred or dollar.**

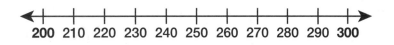

**6.** 205

**7.** $2.78

**8.** 262

**9.** $2.40

_____    _____    _____    _____

**Round to the nearest ten or ten cents.**

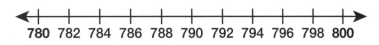

**10.** 787

**11.** $7.93

**12.** 784

**13.** $7.99

_____    _____    _____    _____

## Problem Solving • Reasoning

**14.** Rob has 314 rocks, 215 marbles, and 353 shells. Which of Rob's collections has about 300 items?

**15.** Cheryl has 234 baseball cards, 148 stamps, and 267 buttons. Which of Cheryl's collections has about 200 items?

_____    _____

Name _____     Date _____

# Problem-Solving Skill: Estimated or Exact Amounts

**Solve.**

1. Ceres, the largest known asteroid in our solar system, is about 600 miles across. Is 600 an exact or estimated amount?

   **Think:** Is there a word clue before the number?

   _____

2. California has 52 representatives in the House of Representatives. Do you know exactly how many representatives California has?

   **Think:** Has the number been counted?

   _____

3. There are 7 continents. The largest continent is Asia. It is more than 31 million square miles in area. Do you know exactly how many continents there are?

   _____

4. The Nile crocodile can stay underwater for more than 1 hour waiting to surprise its prey. Is 1 hour an exact or estimated amount?

   _____

**Solve. Use these or other strategies.**

┌─────────────────────────────────────────────────────┐
│              **Problem-Solving Strategies**            │
│  • Draw a Picture    • Write a Number Sentence    • Guess and Check  │
└─────────────────────────────────────────────────────┘

5. Chris bought a shirt and a pair of shorts for $42.00. The shirt cost $10 more than the shorts. How much did the shirt cost?

   _____

6. Chantal can jog a mile in about 12 minutes. About how many minutes will it take Chantal to jog 3 miles?

   _____

7. One U.S. dollar is worth 23 Cuban pesos. How many pesos are 2 U.S. dollars worth?

   _____

8. There are about 9,000 species of birds. Kim saw 8 different species of birds. Which amount is exact?

   _____

Name _____  Date _____

# Modeling One Thousand

| Example |
|---|
| 10 boxes of 50 envelopes |
| less than |

**Tell if each is greater than, less than, or equal to 1,000.**

**1.** 10 bags of 150 push pins

_____

**2.** 100 bags of 100 buttons

_____

**3.** 100 packs of 10 bagels

_____

**4.** 1 pack of 1,000 sheets of paper

_____

**5.** 11 boxes of 10 CDs

_____

**6.** 12 sheets of 100 stickers

_____

**7.** 100 boxes of 8 eggs

_____

**How many of each box is needed in order to have 1,000 letters.**

**8.** Box of 100 letters

_____

**9.** Box of 50 letters

_____

**10.** Box of 1,000 letters

_____

**11.** Box of 250 letters

_____

## Problem Solving • Reasoning

**12.** Mr. Dawson has 9 boxes of 100 cards. He wants to have 1,000 cards. How many more boxes does he need?

_____

**13.** In Kate's class, each group made 20 strips of 10 squares. When all the groups put their squares together, there were 1,000 squares. How many groups were there in Kate's class?

_____

Name _____     Date _____

# Place Value to Thousands

**Example**

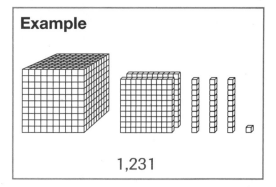

1,231

**Write each number in standard form.**

**1.**

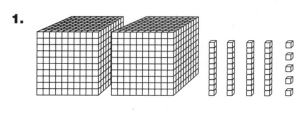

_____

**2.** 4,000 + 300 + 40 + 6

_____

**3.** 5,000 + 8

_____

**4.** three thousand, seven hundred twenty

_____

**5.** eight thousand, five hundred nineteen

_____

**Write the place of the underlined digit. Then write its value.**

**6.** 7,450

_____

**7.** 2,846

_____

**8.** 8,392

_____

**9.** 5,407

_____

**10.** 6,729

_____

**11.** 4,325

_____

**Problem Solving • Reasoning**

**12.** The Golden Gate Bridge in San Francisco spans 1,280 meters. Write this number in expanded form.

_____

**13.** The George Washington Bridge in New York spans one thousand, sixty-seven meters. Write this number in standard form.

_____

Name _____     Date _____

# Compare Numbers

| Example |
|---|
| 94 ◯ 48 |
| > |

**Compare. Write >, <, or = for each ◯.**

**1.** 83 ◯ 38     **2.** 13 ◯ 13     **3.** 23 ◯ 32

**4.** 102 ◯ 120     **5.** 299 ◯ 303     **6.** 348 ◯ 423     **7.** 123 ◯ 123

**8.** 677 ◯ 655     **9.** 743 ◯ 852     **10.** 831 ◯ 813     **11.** 717 ◯ 727

**12.** 380 ◯ 299     **13.** 417 ◯ 500     **14.** 563 ◯ 563     **15.** 983 ◯ 959

**16.** 200 ◯ 189     **17.** 289 ◯ 189     **18.** 397 ◯ 397     **19.** 705 ◯ 800

**20.** 1,247 ◯ 1,347     **21.** 4,589 ◯ 4,590     **22.** 3,153 ◯ 3,134     **23.** 6,101 ◯ 6,101

**24.** 7,532 ◯ 7,479     **25.** 8,150 ◯ 8,139     **26.** 2,509 ◯ 2,510     **27.** 8,009 ◯ 8,200

## Problem Solving • Reasoning

**28.** The Mississippi River is 2,348 miles long. The Missouri River is 2,315 miles long. Which river is longer?

_____

**29.** Maryland has 3,190 miles of shoreline. North Carolina has 3,375 miles of shoreline. Which state has more shoreline?

_____

Name _____  Date _____

# Ordering Numbers

| Example |
|---|
| 76 67 72 |
| 67 72 76 |

**Write the numbers in order from least to greatest.**

**1.** 20 45 34

_____

**2.** 36 24 92

_____

**3.** 215 187 142

_____

**4.** 327 836 217

_____

**5.** 674 823 764

_____

**6.** 1,200 4,315 2,299

_____

**7.** 3,898 5,189 3,198

_____

**8.** 1,947 1,978 1,960

_____

**Write the numbers in order from greatest to least.**

**9.** 53 35 51

_____

**10.** 36 58 18

_____

**11.** 452 450 160

_____

**12.** 327 319 333

_____

**13.** 1,555 1,523 3,527

_____

**14.** 7,347 7,374 7,177

_____

## Problem Solving • Reasoning

**15.**

| Bridge Spans ||
|---|---|
| **Bridge** | **Main Span (in feet)** |
| Benjamin Franklin | 1,750 |
| Walt Whitman | 2,000 |
| Brooklyn Bridge | 1,596 |

Order the spans of the bridges from greatest to least.

_____

**16.**

| Length of Rivers ||
|---|---|
| **River** | **Length (in miles)** |
| Colorado | 1,450 |
| Columbia | 1,243 |
| Rio Grande | 1,900 |

Order the lengths of the rivers from least to greatest.

_____

Name _____ Date _____

# Round Four-Digit Numbers

| Example |
|---|
| 3,873 |
| 4,000 |

**Round to the nearest thousand.**

**1.** 4,320

**2.** 3,401

**3.** 8,762

**4.** 4,299

_____

_____

_____

_____

**5.** 3,500

**6.** 4,782

**7.** 999

**8.** 1,999

**9.** 7,480

_____

_____

_____

_____

_____

**Round to the nearest hundred.**

**10.** 2,489

**11.** 4,713

**12.** 212

**13.** 5,032

**14.** 7,450

_____

_____

_____

_____

_____

**15.** 178

**16.** 801

**17.** 9,065

**18.** 542

**19.** 3,382

_____

_____

_____

_____

_____

**Round to the nearest ten.**

**20.** 7,231

**21.** 353

**22.** 475

**23.** 6,042

**24.** 659

_____

_____

_____

_____

_____

## Problem Solving

Use the table for Exercises 25–26.

**25.** Which states have shorelines that are 3,000 miles long when rounded to the nearest thousand?

_____

**26.** Which states have shorelines that are 3,400 miles long when rounded to the nearest hundred?

_____

| Length of Shorelines | |
|---|---|
| **State** | **Shoreline (miles)** |
| Maine | 3,478 |
| North Carolina | 3,375 |
| South Carolina | 2,876 |
| Texas | 3,359 |
| California | 3,427 |

Name _____   Date _____

# Problem-Solving Strategy: Find a Pattern

**Remember:**
▶ Understand
▶ Plan
▶ Solve
▶ Look Back

Sometimes you can use a pattern to help you solve a problem.

**Solve.**

1. Karen is saving money to buy rollerblades. In March she saved $4. In April she saved $7. In May she saved $10. If this pattern continues, how much money will Karen likely save in June?

   **Think:** How does the amount saved change each month?

   _____

2. There are eight lockers in the hall outside of the science lab. The numbers on the first five lockers are 115, 120, 125, 130, and 135. If the pattern continues, what are the numbers on the next three lockers likely to be?

   **Think:** Which part of the number is changing? How is it changing?

   _____

3. This pattern has six numbers. What is the sixth number likely to be?

   56, 50, 44, 38, 32, _____

   _____

4. What are the next three numbers in the pattern likely to be?

   23, 27, 31, 35, ___, ___, ___

   _____

**Solve. Use these or other strategies.**

---
**Problem-Solving Strategies**

- Write a Number Sentence
- Make a Table
- Use Logical Reasoning
---

5. What is the greatest number that can be made using the digits 4, 2, 3, and 7? The least?

   _____

6. Tickets to the movie theater are $3 for children and $5 for adults. The Stetfield family has two parents and three children. How much will it cost for them all to see a movie?

   _____

Name _____  Date _____

# Place Value to Ten Thousands

| Example |
|---|
| 50,000 + 200 + 4 |
| 50,204 |

**Write each number in standard form.**

**1.** four thousand, thirty-five

_____

**2.** forty-one thousand, two hundred nine

_____

**3.** 2 ten thousands 4 hundreds 7 ones

_____

**4.** 40,000 + 3,000 + 100 + 60 + 2

_____

**5.** fifty thousand, three hundred twelve

_____

**Write the place value of the underlined digit. Then write its value.**

**6.** <u>7</u>0

_____

**7.** 33,<u>3</u>33

_____

**8.** <u>4</u>8,203

_____

**9.** 7<u>3</u>,541

_____

## Problem Solving • Reasoning

Use the table for Problem 10.

**10.** Round the average depth of the Pacific Ocean, Atlantic Ocean, and Indian Ocean to the nearest thousand. What do you notice?

_____

_____

| Ocean Depths | |
|---|---|
| **Ocean** | **Average Depth (in ft)** |
| Pacific Ocean | 13,215 |
| Atlantic Ocean | 12,880 |
| Indian Ocean | 13,002 |
| Arctic Ocean | 3,953 |

Name _____    Date _____

# Place Value to Hundred Thousands

| Example |
|---|
| 300,000 + 4,000 + 900 + 50 + 2 |
| 304,952 |

**Write each number in standard form.**

**1.** four hundred thousand, five hundred four

_____

**2.** two hundred three thousand, seventy-one

_____

**3.** 800,000 + 700 + 40

_____

**4.** 600,000 + 50,000 + 200 + 40 + 9

_____

**5.** six hundred twenty-one thousand, five hundred twenty-four

_____

**Write the place of the underlined digit. Then write its value.**

**6.** 528,341

_____

**7.** 317,924

_____

**8.** 576,421

_____

**9.** 147,826

_____

## Problem Solving • Reasoning

**10.** The Bering Sea has an area of 884,900 square miles. What value does the digit 4 have?

_____

**11.** Greenland, with an area of 839,999 square miles, is the largest island in the world. What value does the digit 8 have?

_____

Name _____ Date _____

# Problem-Solving Application: Read a Graph

You can get information from a graph to help you solve problems.

**Use the graph for Exercises 1–4.**

**1.** About how much taller is the Sears Tower than the John Hancock Center?

**Think:** How can each height be rounded to the nearest hundred?

_____

**2.** Which two buildings are about the same height?

**Think:** Which bars are about the same height?

_____

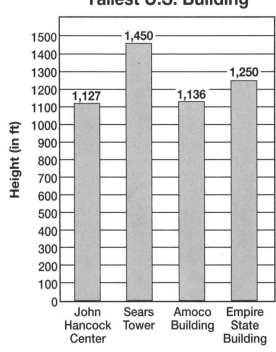

**Tallest U.S. Building**

**3.** About how much taller is the Empire State Building than the John Hancock Center?

_____

**4.** Suppose a building was as tall as the Sears Tower and the Amoco Building together. About how tall would the building be?

_____

**Solve. Use these or other strategies.**

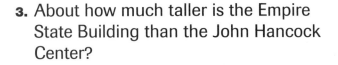

**Problem-Solving Strategies**

| • Guess and Check | • Write a Number Sentence | • Use Logical Thinking |

**5.** Dee bought a sweater and a shirt for $40.00. The sweater cost $12 more than the shirt. How much did the shirt cost?

_____

**6.** Kim's family drove about 50 miles in the first hour of their trip. About how many miles will they drive in 3 hours?

_____

Name _____ Date _____

# Value of Money

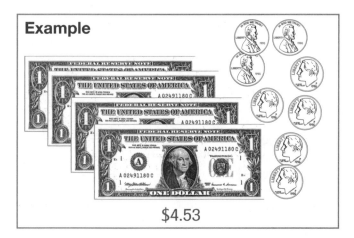

**Example**

$4.53

**Write each amount, using a dollar sign and decimal point.**

**1.**

_____

**2.**

_____

**3.**

_____

**4.** seven dollars and thirty-nine cents

_____

**5.** four dollars and sixteen cents

_____

## Problem Solving • Reasoning

**6.** Caroline has $3.20 in her bank. How much will she have if she puts 1 dollar, 3 dimes, and 6 pennies into her bank?

_____

**7.** Ray has 10 dimes and 40 pennies in his bank. He doubles the amount of dimes and pennies. What is the value of the money in Ray's bank now?

_____

Name _____   Date _____

# Count Coins and Bills

**Example**

$1.62

**Write each amount, using a dollar sign and decimal point.**

**1.**

_____

**2.**

_____

**3.**

_____

**4.** 5 half-dollars, 2 dimes, and 4 pennies

_____

**5.** 3 one-dollar bills, 3 half-dollars, and 9 nickels

_____

## Problem Solving • Reasoning

**6.** Dan has 3 quarters, 4 dimes, and 5 nickels. Angela has 2 quarters, 6 dimes, and 8 nickels. Who has less money?

_____

**7.** Cameron gets 1 five-dollar bill and 5 dimes for allowance each week. How much money does he get for 2 weeks?

_____

Name _____ Date _____

# Equivalent Amounts

| Example |
| --- |
| 3 five-dollar bills and five dimes<br>B |

**Write the value of the amount for each exercise on the left. Then write the letter of its equivalent amount at the right.**

**1.** 2 one-dollar bills, 1 dollar coin, and 9 nickels

_____

**A.**

**2.** 15 one-dollar bills, 1 quarter, and 5 nickels

_____

**B.**

**3.** 1 one-dollar bill, 1 dime, and 1 nickel

_____

**C.**

**4.** 2 quarters, 5 dimes, and 15 pennies

_____

## Problem Solving • Reasoning

**5.** Stephen needs $12 to buy a book. He has 7 one-dollar bills, 11 quarters, 5 dimes, and 7 pennies. Does he have enough to buy the book?

_____

**6.** Matt gives his little sister 45¢ to buy a postcard. He gives his sister three coins. What coins does she have?

_____

Name _____ Date _____

# Count Change

**Example**

You paid with $1.00.

**$0.55**

2 dimes, 1 quarter; $0.45

**Find the correct change. List the coins and bills used.**

**1.** You paid with $5.00.

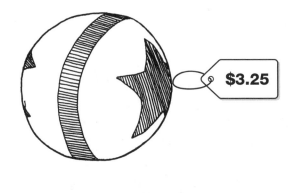

**$3.25**

_____

**2.** You paid with 75¢. You bought a pencil for $0.60.

_____

**3.** You paid with $10.00. You bought a card game for $8.65.

_____

**Complete the table below. List the coins and bills you might get as change.**

| | Amount Paid | Cost of Item | Change |
|---|---|---|---|
| **4.** | $1.00 | 49¢ | |
| **5.** | $10.00 | $2.69 | |
| **6.** | $15.00 | $12.50 | |

## Problem Solving • Reasoning

**7.** Sophie bought flowers. She gave the clerk $10.00. She received $2.50 from the clerk. How much were the flowers?

_____

**8.** John bought a card for $1.45 and gift wrap for $1.00. He gave the cashier $5.00. How much change did he receive?

_____

Name _____ Date _____

# Problem-Solving Skill: Choose the Operation

Sometimes you need to decide whether to add or subtract to solve a problem.

**Solve.**

**1.** Hannah works at the library. On Tuesday she checked out 54 books. On Thursday, she checked out 49 books. How many more books did Hannah check out on Tuesday?

**Think:** Do I need to find the total amount or part of the amount?

_____

**2.** Hannah spent Wednesday reshelving books. Before lunch she reshelved 28 books. After lunch she reshelved 41 books. How many books did Hannah reshelve on Wednesday?

**Think:** Do I need to find the total amount or part of the amount?

_____

**3.** On Monday Hannah had to collect fines for overdue books. She collected $17 in fines. The previous Monday she had collected $8 in fines. How much more did Hannah collect this week?

_____

**4.** Hannah arranged two display cabinets with new videotapes. In one cabinet she put 34 new videotapes. In the other she put 25 new videotapes. How many new videotapes did Hannah use in her displays?

_____

### Problem-Solving Strategies

- Use Logical Thinking
- Find a Pattern
- Write a Number Sentence

**5.** Alice, Brad, Charlene, and Dave line up in order of heights. A girl is the tallest. Dave stands next to Charlene. Brad is taller than Dave. Charlene is the shortest. Write the names of the students in order from shortest to tallest.

_____

**6.** Jason was shopping for a new shirt. The first two shirts in the stack were blue, the next two were green, and then there was a white one. Then he saw 2 more blue shirts, 2 green shirts, a white shirt, and a blue one. What color is the next shirt?

_____

Name _____  Date _____

# Hour, Half-Hour, Quarter-Hour

**Example**

eight-thirty, thirty minutes after eight, half past eight, 8:30

**Write each time in at least two ways.**

**1.**

_____

**2.**

_____

**3.**

_____

**Write each time using numbers.**

**4.** fifteen minutes after two

_____

**5.** nine-thirty

_____

**6.** four o'clock

_____

**7.** fifteen minutes before twelve

_____

## Problem Solving • Reasoning

**8.** Tim arrived at school at 7:35 A.M. Rob arrived at school at seven-thirty. Who arrived at school first?

_____

**9.** The play was scheduled to start at 8:00. Charlise arrived 15 minutes early. What time did she arrive?

_____

Name _____     Date _____

# Time to Five Minutes

**Example**

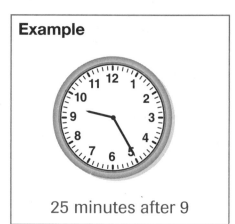

25 minutes after 9

**Write each time as minutes after or before the hour.**

1.

_____

_____

2.

_____

3.

_____

_____

**Compare. Write >, <, or = in each ◯.**

4. 35 minutes ◯ 1 half hour

5. 1 quarter hour ◯ 15 minutes

6. 100 minutes ◯ 1 hour

7. 45 minutes ◯ 1 hour

**Complete. Use _minutes_, _hours_, or _days_.**

8. Walking the dog takes about 20 _____.

9. Playing a soccer game takes about 2 _____.

**Problem Solving • Reasoning**

10. Lou arrives at a bus stop. A friend tells him the bus was there at 12:25. The bus comes every 15 minutes. What time will the next bus arrive?

11. Jennie wants to see a play that starts at 7:00 P.M. She has a piano lesson that lasts until 6:45 P.M. Can she go to the play and the lesson?

_____

_____

Name _____  Date _____

# Time to the Minute

| **Example** 5:29 |
|---|
| five twenty-nine |

**Write each time in words.**

**1.** 6:56

_____

**2.** 12:16

_____

**3.** 8:34

_____

**4.** 10:25

_____

**5.** 3:12

_____

**Write each time as minutes after and before the hour.**

**6.**

_____

**7.**

_____

## Problem Solving • Reasoning

**8.** It is 42 minutes after 3. Scott has soccer practice at 4:15. How many minutes does he have until soccer practice starts?

_____

**9.** Dan and Chris both started jogging at 5:00. Dan stopped jogging at 45 minutes after 5. Christine stopped jogging at 10 minutes before 6. Who jogged for a longer period of time?

_____

Name _____ Date _____

# Problem-Solving Strategy: Use Logical Thinking

Sometimes you need to use logical thinking to solve a problem.

**Solve.**

1. Mrs. Parker's class is going on a trip to a historical village. Bill, Jim, and Cleo are wearing hats. Bill wears neither the cap nor the visor. Jim wore the visor. Cleo doesn't wear the sombrero. What did each student wear?

   **Think:** What do I know? How can I organize this information?

   _____

2. At the schoolhouse exhibit, Jack, Cliff, and Rose pretended to be students of the past. Jack did a math problem on his slate. The student who recited a poem wore a skirt. Who wrote the spelling list?

   **Think:** What do I know? Does my answer match the facts?

   _____

3. Mitzi, Ben, Sarah, and Howard each had favorite exhibits. Neither Mitzi nor Howard liked the printshop. Sarah didn't like the leather shop. Ben liked the blacksmith best. A boy liked the weaver best. What did Mitzi like best?

   _____

4. Shanna, Liz, and Richard were asked to line up by height. A girl was tallest. Neither Richard nor Shanna were the shortest. Write the students' names in order from tallest to shortest.

   _____

### Problem-Solving Strategies

| • Find a Pattern | • Use Logical Thinking | • Act It Out |
|---|---|---|

5. Jerry went to the grocery to buy water. Each large bottle cost $2. Jerry bought 15 bottles. How much did Jerry spend on bottled water?

   _____

6. On Monday George unpacked 27 new computers. On Tuesday, he unpacked 35 new computers. How many more computers did George unpack on Tuesday than on Monday?

   _____

Name _____  Date _____

# Elapsed Time

| | |
|---|---|
| **Example** | **Tell what time it will be.** |
| in 20 minutes | **1.** in 25 minutes |

3:35

_____

**2.** in 30 minutes

**3.** in 4 hours

_____        _____

**Look at each pair of times. Write how much time has elapsed.**

**4.** Start: 2:20 P.M.
   End:  2:45 P.M.

**5.** Start: 1:05 P.M.
   End:  1:45 P.M.

**6.** Start: 7:55 A.M.
   End:  8:55 A.M.

_____        _____        _____

## Problem Solving • Reasoning

**7.** Elaine has the flu. She takes medicine every 4 hours. Elaine takes the medicine at 7:00 A.M. When should she take the next dose?

**8.** Chuck practices the saxophone for 45 minutes each day. If he starts practicing at 3:30, when will he stop?

_____        _____

Name _____     Date _____

# Use a Calendar

| Example |
|---|
| What date is the Craft Show? |
| April 14 |

1. What day of the week is April 12?

   _____

2. What is the date of the third Thursday?

   _____

**Use the April calendar for Exercises 1–4.**

### April

| Sunday | Monday | Tuesday | Wednesday | Thursday | Friday | Saturday |
|---|---|---|---|---|---|---|
| | | | | | | 1 |
| 2 | 3 | 4 | 5 | 6 | 7 | 8 |
| 9 | 10 | 11 | 12 | 13 | Craft Show 14 | 15 |
| 16 | 17 | 18 | 19 | 20 | 21 | 22 |
| 23 | 24 | 25 | 26 | 27 | 28 | 29 |
| 30 | | | | | | |

3. What is the date 2 weeks after April 3?

   _____

4. Write the ordinal number for the last Saturday in April.

   _____

Name the month that is 3 months after each month.

5. April

   _____

6. January

   _____

7. November

   _____

## Problem Solving • Reasoning

**Use the calendar above for Problems 8 and 9.**

8. Daniel wants to have a party on a Saturday night in April. He will be away on April 22. His parents are having a party on April 1. What nights could he have the party?

   _____

9. Cindy's family is taking a two-week trip to the mountains. They are leaving on April 10. What date will they return?

   _____

Name _____     Date _____

# Problem-Solving Application: Use a Schedule

Remember:
► Understand
► Plan
► Solve
► Look Back

A schedule is a table that lists the times for events or activities.

**Daily Movies**

| Movie | Starting Time | Ending Time |
|-------|---------------|-------------|
| Maximum Lift | 1:00 P.M. | 2:30 P.M. |
| Big League | 3:25 P.M. | 5:05 P.M. |
| Great White | 3:00 P.M. | 5:10 P.M. |

**Solve.**

1. What movies start between 2:45 P.M. and 3:45 P.M.?

   **Think:** Do the movies have to start at 2:45 and 3:45?

   _____

2. Is it possible to see more than one movie on the same day? Explain.

   **Think:** How many of the movies are shown at the same time?

   _____

**Solve. Use these and other strategies.**

## Problem-Solving Strategies

- Find a Pattern
- Use Logical Thinking
- Make a Table

3. Ann, Joe, and Jill each play a sport. The sports are football, swimming, and tennis. Ann does not need a racquet. Joe wears a helmet. Jill does not need goggles. Who plays tennis?

   _____

4. Peter mowed Mr. Watson's lawn on Monday, May 5. Mr. Watson asked Peter to come back in 15 days to mow his lawn again. What day of the week will Peter return to Mr. Watson's?

   _____

Name _____  Date _____

# Addition Properties

| Example |
|---|
| 4 |
| 9 |
| + 6 |
| **19** |
| (4 + 9) + 6 = 19 |

**Add.**

**1.**   5
       0
     + 8
    _____

**2.**   9
       4
     + 2
    _____

**3.**   3
       7
     + 0
    _____

**4.**   2
       9
     + 1
    _____

**5.**   8
       3
     + 5
    _____

**6.** $3 + 4 + 7 + 4$

_____

**7.** $4 + 5 + (6 + 2 + 2)$

_____

**8.** $2 + (8 + 4) + 5 + 6$

_____

**Find the missing numbers.**

**9.** $8 + 7 = 7 +$ _____

_____

**10.** $12 +$ _____ $= 12$

_____

**11.** $9 + 6 =$ _____ $+ 9$

_____

**12.** $0 +$ _____ $= 11$

_____

**13.** $8 + 4 + 2 =$ _____
     $+ 4 + 8$

_____

**14.** $7 + 5 + 4 = 4 +$ _____
      $+ 7$

_____

## Problem Solving • Reasoning

**15.** Patricia picked vegetables from her garden. She picked 3 tomatoes, 4 cucumbers, 5 peppers, and 7 squash. How many vegetables did she pick?

_____

**16.** Glenn bought balloons for his brother's birthday party. He bought 5 red balloons, 4 yellow balloons, and 5 green balloons. Then 1 balloon popped. How many balloons did Glenn have then?

_____

Name _____ Date _____

# Regroup Ones

| Example |
|---|
| 48<br>+ 23<br>yes |

**Write *yes* for the exercises where you will need to regroup ones to make a ten.**

**1.** 55<br>+ 43

**2.** 67<br>+ 21

**3.** 89<br>+ 16

**4.** 136<br>+ 209

**Add. Then estimate to check that your answers are reasonable.**

**5.** $47<br>+ $36

**6.** 62<br>+ 29

**7.** 106<br>+ 239

**8.** 408<br>+ 277

**9.** 276<br>+ 315

**Complete each table by following the rule.**

**10. Rule: Add 37**

| Input | Output |
|---|---|
| 27 | |
| 49 | |
| 56 | |

**11. Rule: Add 145**

| Input | Output |
|---|---|
| 319 | |
| 108 | |
| 635 | |

## Problem Solving • Reasoning

**12.** There are 119 types of fish and 114 types of reptiles. How many types of fish and reptiles are there?

_____

**13.** On Saturday morning, 219 people visited the reptile exhibit. In the afternoon, 383 people visited the exhibit. About how many people visited the exhibit on Saturday?

_____

Name _____   Date _____

# Regroup Ones and Tens

| Example |
|---|
| 237 |
| + 459 |
| 696 |

**Add. Check by estimating or adding up.**

**1.** 289
+ 327

**2.** $5.47
+ 2.66

**3.** 772
+ 198

**4.** 142
+ 105

**5.** $2.87
+ 4.89

**6.** 477
+ 368

**7.** 567
+ 276

**8.** 649
+ 285

**9.** 448
+ 183

**10.** 234
+ 498

**11.** 421
+ 499

**12.** 584
+ 377

**13.** 498
+ 325

**14.** 345
+ 378

**15.** $3.57
+ 3.76

**16.** 452
+ 279

**17.** 536
+ 285

**18.** 559
+ 179

**19.** 238
+ 395

**20.** 464
+ 397

**21.** 375
+ 225

**22.** 556
+ 178

**23.** 757
+ 148

**24.** 643
+ 199

## Problem Solving • Reasoning

**25.** Bud made 129 deliveries in January and 196 deliveries in February. How many deliveries did he make during these two months?

_____

**26.** Bud's Flower Shop sold 115 more roses than carnations. If the shop sold 297 carnations, how many carnations and roses did they sell?

_____

Name _____   Date _____

# Estimate Sums

| Example |
|---|
| 56 rounds to    60 |
| + 72 rounds to + 70 |
|             130 |

**Round each number to the greatest place. Then add.**

1.    28
   + 31

2.    67
   + 19

3.    37
   + 68

4.    52
   + 12

5.    78
   + 92

6.    38
   + 49

7.    23
   + 38

8.    51
   + 26

9.    45
   + 79

10.    427
   + 389

11.    677
   + 210

12.    537
   + 192

13.    412
   + 537

14.    634
   + 485

15.    $3.79
   + 2.19

16.    278
   + 128

17.    218
   + 498

18.    186
   + 432

19.    925
   + 110

20.    367
   + 512

21.    $7.23
   + 1.67

22.    268
   + 389

23.    710
   + 112

24.    312
   + 259

25.    223
   + 479

26.    589
   + 312

27.    678
   + 115

28.    779
   + 102

## Problem Solving • Reasoning

29. Christina's lunch cost $8.15 and Timothy's lunch cost $7.87. About how much did both lunches cost?

30. Shana biked 32 miles Saturday and 35 miles Sunday. About how many miles did she bike over the weekend?

Name _____     Date _____

# Problem-Solving Skill: Exact Answer or Estimate

Sometimes you need to decide whether you need an estimate or an exact answer.

**Use the information. Decide whether you need an estimate or an exact answer. Then solve.**

In California, Feather Waterfall is 323 feet higher than Vernal Waterfall. Vernal Waterfall is 317 feet high.

**1.** How high is Feather Waterfall?

**Think:** How high is Vernal Waterfall?

_____

**2.** About how tall is Feather Waterfall?

**Think:** Can you estimate to solve?

_____

Connecticut has 234 more miles of tidal shoreline than Rhode Island. Rhode Island has 384 miles of tidal shoreline. New Hampshire has 131 miles of tidal shoreline.

**3.** About how many miles of tidal shoreline do Rhode Island and New Hampshire have together?

_____

**4.** How many miles of tidal shoreline does Connecticut have?

_____

**Solve. Use these or other strategies.**

| Problem-Solving Strategies |
| --- |
| • Draw a Picture  • Use Logical Thinking  • Write a Number Sentence |

**5.** One U.S. dollar is worth 23 Cuban pesos. Lin has 2 dollars. Can she buy a map that costs 50 pesos? Explain.

_____

**6.** Trina walks three blocks east, two blocks north, two blocks west, and two blocks south. How many blocks is Trina from where she started?

_____

Name _____   Date _____

# Problem-Solving Strategy: Guess and Check

Remember:
► Understand
► Plan
► Solve
► Look Back

Knowing how to use the Guess and Check strategy will help you solve problems.

**Use the Guess and Check strategy to solve each problem.**

**1.** A grizzly bear's life span is 7 years more than a black bear's life span. The sum of their life spans is 43 years. What is the life span of the grizzly bear and the black bear?

**Think:** What should the sum of the two numbers be?

_____

**2.** Jason and Audre both collect animal cards. Jason has 22 more cards than Audre. Together they have 112 cards. How many animal cards does Jason have? How many cards does Audre have?

**Think:** How much larger should one number be than the other?

_____

**3.** Gina made 7 more animal models than Mandy. Together, Gina and Mandy made 31 models. How many animal models did Gina make? How many models did Mandy made?

_____

**4.** Lisa has 12 more fish than Danielle. Together they have 38 fish. How many fish does Lisa have? How many fish does Danielle have?

_____

**Solve. Use these or other strategies.**

**Problem-Solving Strategies**

• Guess and Check    • Use Logical Thinking    • Write a Number Sentence

**5.** Jay made four stops on his way home. First, he stopped at the library. He stopped at Glen's house after he went to the store, but before he stopped at Ned's house. List Jay's stops in order from first to last.

_____

**6.** Casey ran for 20 minutes longer than he biked. If he biked for 37 minutes, how long did he run?

_____

Name _____ Date _____

# Subtraction Strategies and Properties

| Example | | |
|---|---|---|
| 7 | 5 | 6 |
| − 0 | − 5 | − 5 |
| 0 | 0 | 1 |

**Subtract.**

1.  9
   − 6

2.  8
   − 7

3.  7
   − 3

4.  9
   − 0

5.  9
   − 6

6.  4
   − 4

7.  5
   − 2

8.  8
   − 0

9.  6
   − 4

10. $8 - 8$

11. $9 - 2$

12. $7 - 3$

13. $9 - 9$

**Find each missing number.**

14. $7 - \rule{1.5cm}{0.4pt} = 7$

15. $\rule{1.5cm}{0.4pt} - 6 = 0$

16. $8 - \rule{1.5cm}{0.4pt} = 0$

17. $7 - 7 = \rule{1.5cm}{0.4pt}$

18. $\rule{1.5cm}{0.4pt} - 0 = 4$

19. $3 - 0 = \rule{1.5cm}{0.4pt}$

20. $\rule{1.5cm}{0.4pt} - 2 = 0$

21. $1 - \rule{1.5cm}{0.4pt} = 0$

22. $9 - 0 = \rule{1.5cm}{0.4pt}$

23. $\rule{1.5cm}{0.4pt} - 0 = 5$

24. $4 - \rule{1.5cm}{0.4pt} = 0$

25. $8 - \rule{1.5cm}{0.4pt} = 8$

## Problem Solving • Reasoning

26. Cameron had 8 stickers. He gave 3 to Jackie. How many stickers does Cameron have left?

27. Stuart gives 4 of his baseball caps to friends. If Stuart had 8 baseball caps, how many does he have now?

Name _____ Date _____

# Regroup Tens

| Example |
|---|
| 678<br>− 549<br>──<br>yes |

**Write *yes* for the exercises where you will need to regroup a ten to make 10 ones.**

**1.** 859<br>− 246

**2.** 749<br>− 434

**3.** 328<br>− 119

**4.** 274<br>− 196

**Subtract. Then estimate to check that your answers are reasonable.**

**5.** $46<br>− 28

**6.** 73<br>− 47

**7.** 53<br>− 15

**8.** 61<br>− 34

**9.** 33<br>− 18

**10.** 446<br>− 229

**11.** 385<br>− 137

**12.** 752<br>− 436

**13.** $8.21<br>− 6.07

**14.** 854<br>− 537

**15.** $82 − $37

**16.** 73 − 18

**17.** 63 − 47

**18.** 928 − 419

**19.** 746 − 217

**20.** 470 − 216

## Problem Solving • Reasoning

**21.** Susan collected 435 cans for the recyling drive. She brought 149 cans to the center. How many cans does she still have?

**22.** Nathan's class did 225 hours of community service. Heather's class did 312 hours. How many more hours of community service did Heather's class do?

Name _____     Date _____

# Regroup Tens and Hundreds

| Example |
|---|
| 487 |
| − 299 |
| 188 |

**Subtract. Check by adding.**

**1.**  746
− 258

**2.**  $4.73
− 2.77

**3.**  783
− 584

**4.**  932
− 654

**5.**  $7.25
− 4.87

**6.**  $8.37
− 4.79

**7.**  517
− 278

**8.**  646
− 428

**9.**  327
− 138

**10.**  837
− 198

**11.**  545
− 276

**12.**  921
− 743

**13.**  412
− 235

**14.**  624
− 357

**15.** 567 − 379

**16.** 344 − 158

**17.** 562 − 378

**18.** 325 − 147

**19.** 823 − 455

**20.** 457 − 279

**21.** 532 − 275

**22.** 468 − 169

**23.** $4.67 − $2.78

**24.** 783 − 387

**25.** 731 − 276

**26.** 671 − 386

## Problem Solving • Reasoning

**27.** The school sold 335 tickets for the play on Saturday night. One hundred thirty-nine tickets were sold for Sunday afternoon. How many more tickets were sold for the Saturday performance?

**28.** The school spent $195 on costumes and $135 for sets. How much more money did they spend on costumes?

Name _____ Date _____

# Estimate Differences

| Example |
|---|
| 73 rounds to   70 |
| − 52 rounds to − 50 |
| 20 |

**Round each number to the greatest place. Then estimate.**

**1.**   59
− 18

**2.**   38
− 21

**3.**   63
− 31

**4.**   87
− 31

**5.**   68
− 21

**6.**   88
− 12

**7.**   39
− 11

**8.**   46
− 33

**9.**   923
− 398

**10.**   779
− 424

**11.**   689
− 316

**12.**   509
− 287

**13.**   726
− 378

**14.**   289
− 113

**15.**   827
− 314

**16.**   731
− 287

**17.**   824
− 384

**18.**   423
− 234

## Problem Solving • Reasoning

**19.** Jefferson Grade School has 489 students. Walcott Grade School has 612 students. About how many more students does Walcott have?

**20.** There are 331 children at early lunch at Jefferson school. There are 229 children at late lunch. How many more children are at early lunch?

Name _____    Date _____

# Subtract Greater Numbers

| Example |
|---|
| $\overset{6\ 2\ 1}{5,7\cancel{3}4}$ |
| $-\ 2,398$ |
| $3,336$ |

**Find each difference. Check by adding.**

**1.**     7,635
      − 2,488

**2.**     6,783
      − 4,527

**3.**     $78.34
      − 23.57

**4.**     3,378
      − 1,968

**5.**     6,766
      − 4,578

**6.**     8,633
      − 4,711

**7.**     7,462
      − 4,297

**8.**     6,872
      − 3,451

**9.**     4,219
      − 2,764

**10.**    7,231
      − 6,187

**11.**    8,374
      − 4,286

**12.**    $51.97
      − 24.95

**13.**    8,837
      − 5,929

**14.**    7,362
      − 3,841

**15.**    4,719
      − 2,428

**16.**    7,381
      − 5,153

**17.**    5,674
      − 2,792

**18.**    6,435
      − 4,547

**19.**    4,739
      − 3,247

## Problem Solving • Reasoning

**20.** A shirt was priced at $12.99. Corinne buys it on sale for $11.50. How much does she save?

_____

**21.** Sal's Sale Barn has 239 T-shirts and 452 dress shirts in stock. How many more dress shirts do they have in stock?

_____

Name _____    Date _____

# Subtract Across Zeros

| Example |
|---|
| 4 10 |
| 5̶0̶8 |
| − 362 |
| 146 |

**Subtract. Check by using addition or estimation.**

**1.**  903
      − 467

**2.**  700
      − 373

**3.**  400
      − 128

**4.**  608
      − 287

**5.**  6,001
      − 3,340

**6.**  2,704
      − 1,372

**7.**  7,503
      − 3,429

**8.**  6,400
      − 3,183

**9.**  5,203
      − 2,163

**10.**  2,004
       − 1,491

**11.**  5,800
       − 2,434

**12.**  7,800
       − 2,912

**13.**  5,078
       − 2,493

**14.**  3,502
       − 1,488

**15.** 505 − 436

**16.** 800 − 378

**17.** 600 − 271

**18.** 3,804 − 1,482

**19.** 7,700 − 7,291

**20.** 5,003 − 3,421

## Problem Solving • Reasoning

**21.** The largest reptile is the saltwater crocodile, which weighs 1,150 pounds. The largest bird is the ostrich, which weighs 345 pounds. How much heavier is the largest reptile than the largest bird?

**22.** During the first week, 4,532 people visit the reptile exhibit at the zoo. The second week, 6,400 people visit. How many more people visit during the second week?

Name _____  Date _____

# Problem-Solving Application: Use Operations

Remember:
► Understand
► Plan
► Solve
► Look Back

Sometimes you must decide whether to use addition or subtraction to solve a problem.

**Solve each problem.**

**1.** There are 61 endangered mammals in the United States. There are 75 endangered birds. How many more birds are endangered than mammals?

**Think:** Do I need to find the total amount or am I comparing amounts?

_____

**2.** A male peacock has 200 long feathers. How many long feathers do 2 peacocks have?

**Think:** Do I need to find the total amount or am I comparing amounts?

_____

**3.** The lion lives for an average of 10 years. The goat lives for 12 years. How many more years does the goat live?

_____

**4.** A rhinoceros carries its young for 650 days. A cow carries its young for 283 days. How much longer does the rhinoceros carry its young?

_____

**Solve. Use these or other strategies.**

### Problem-Solving Strategies

| • Find a Pattern | • Guess and Check | • Write a Number Sequence |

**5.** A lion can travel 20 miles per hour faster than a giraffe. A giraffe can travel 30 miles per hour. How fast can a lion travel?

_____

**6.** Michael has $3 more than John. Together they have $27. How much money does each boy have?

_____

Name _____  Date _____

# Measuring Length

**Example**

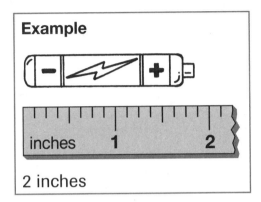

2 inches

Use a ruler. Measure the length of each object to the nearest inch.

1.

_____

3.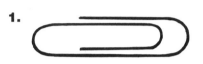

_____

2.

_____

4.

_____

5.

_____

## Problem-Solving • Reasoning

6. Maria's pencil measures a little more than two and a half inches. What is the length of the pencil to the nearest inch?

_____

7. **Write About It** Describe how you measured the objects and how you determined the lengths to the nearest inch.

_____

Name _____   Date _____

# Measure to the Nearest Half Inch

**Example**

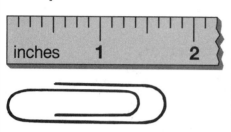

To the nearest half inch, this paper clip is 2 inches long.

**Measure each object to the nearest half inch.**

1.

_____

2.

_____

3.

_____

4.

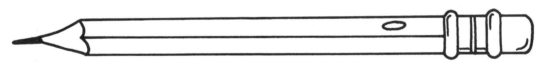

_____

**Use an inch ruler. Draw a line of each length.**

5. $2\frac{1}{2}$ in.

6. $3\frac{1}{2}$ in.

7. $2\frac{1}{2}$ in.

8. 4 in.

## Problem Solving • Reasoning

9. Andrew has a miniature model train. The engine is $3\frac{1}{2}$ in. long. The caboose is 1 in. shorter. How long is the caboose?

_____

10. One piece of train track measures $5\frac{1}{2}$ inches. One end lies on the zero mark of the ruler. Between which two inch marks on the ruler does the other end of the track lie?

_____

Name _____ Date _____

# Customary Units of Length

| Example |
|---|
| the height of a man |
| **ⓐ** 6 feet    **b.** 6 miles |

**Choose the better estimate. Circle the answers.**

1. the length of a piece of paper

   **a.** 11 yards    **b.** 11 inches

2. the height of a tree

   **a.** 50 feet    **b.** 50 inches

3. the height of a skyscraper

   **a.** 1,000 miles    **b.** 1,000 yards

4. the length of a pair of pants

   **a.** 1 inch    **b.** 1 yard

5. the length of a roll of kite string

   **a.** 300 yards    **b.** 300 miles

**Find the missing measure.**

6. 1 yd = _____ ft

7. 1 ft = _____ in.

8. 36 in. = _____ ft

9. 15 ft = _____ yd

10. 24 in. = _____ ft

11. 1 yd = _____ in.

12. 9 ft = _____ yd

13. 5 ft = _____ in.

14. 5,280 ft = _____ mi

## Problem Solving • Reasoning

15. Becky and Ned made banners. Becky's banner is 2 yards long. Ned's banner is 6 feet long. Which banner is the longest? Explain how you got your answer.

_____

_____

_____

16. Aly and Hilary measured how far they could jump. Aly's jump measured 1 yard. Hilary's jump measured 38 inches. Who jumped the farthest? Explain how you got your answer.

_____

_____

_____

Name _____ Date _____

# Estimating and Measuring Capacity

**Use the table to find the missing measure.**

|        | **Pint** | **Quart** | **Gallon** |
|--------|----------|-----------|------------|
| Cups   | 2        | 4         | 16         |
| Pints  |          | 2         | 8          |
| Quarts |          |           | 4          |

**Example**

1 qt = 4 c

**1.** 2 pt = _____ qt

**2.** 1 gal = _____ qt

**3.** 16 c = _____ gal

**4.** 1 gal = _____ pt

**5.** 8 pt = _____ qt

**6.** 4 pt = _____ qt

**7.** 2 qt = _____ c

**8.** 2 gal = _____ qt

**9.** 2 pt = _____ c

**10.** 3 qt = _____ pt

**11.** 3 pt = _____ c

**12.** 8 c = _____ qt

**13.** 32 c = _____ gal

**14.** 2 gal = _____ pt

## Write About It

**15.** You know that there are 2 pints in a quart. You know there are 4 quarts in a gallon. How can you find the number of pints in a gallon without measuring?

_____

_____

_____

**16.** Suppose you need to pour 2 gallons of juice into pint containers. How many pint containers would you need? Explain how you determined the number.

_____

_____

_____

Name _____ Date _____

# Customary Units of Capacity

**Example**

gallon

Choose the unit you would use to measure the capacity of each. Write *cup, pint, quart,* or *gallon.*

**1.**

_____

**2.**

_____

**3.**

_____

**4.**

_____

**5.**

_____

**Find the missing measure.**

**6.** 2 c = _____ pt

**7.** 8 pt = _____ gal

**8.** 4 c = _____ qt

**9.** 8 c = _____ qt

**10.** 2 qt = _____ pt

**11.** 2 gal = _____ c

## Problem Solving • Reasoning

**12.** Jacob has a 2-quart pitcher. He uses a 1-pint container to fill the pitcher. How many times must he fill the 1-pint container to fill the pitcher?

_____

**13.** A recipe calls for $1\frac{1}{2}$ cups of milk. How many cups of milk do you need to double the recipe?

_____

Name _____ Date _____

# Customary Units of Weight

| Example |
|---|
| 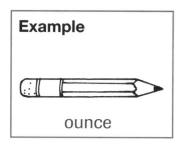 |
| ounce |

**Choose the unit that you would use to measure the weight of each. Write *ounce* or *pound*.**

1.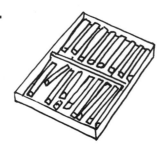

_____

2.

_____

3. bowling ball

_____

4. tennis ball

_____

5. dog

_____

**Choose the better estimate. Circle the answer.**

6. a cat
   **a.** 6 pounds
   **b.** 6 ounces

7. a loaf of bread
   **a.** 1 pound
   **b.** 1 ounce

8. a bicycle
   **a.** 25 ounces
   **b.** 25 pounds

**Find the missing measure.**

9. 8 oz = _____ lb

10. 2 lb = _____ oz

11. 16 oz = _____ lb

**Problem Solving • Reasoning**

12. Lucy is buying apples. One bag has 2 pounds of apples. Another bag has 28 ounces of apples. Which bag is heavier? How much heavier is it than the other bag?

_____

13. Andy needs 20 ounces of flour to make one batch of cookies. He buys a 5-pound bag of flour. How many batches of cookies can he make?

_____

Name _____  Date _____

# Temperature: Degrees Fahrenheit

**Example**

42°F; cool

Write each temperature. Then write *hot, warm, cool,* or *cold* to describe the temperature.

**1.**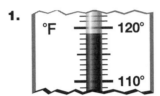

_____

**2.**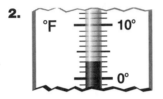

_____

**3.**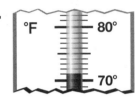

_____

**4.**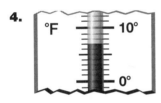

_____

**5.**

_____

**6.**

_____

**7.**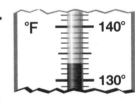

_____

Choose the better estimate of the temperature.
Circle the answer.

**8.**

**a.** 88°F   **b.** 32°F

**9.**

**a.** 20°F   **b.** 95°F

**10.**

**a.** 72°F   **b.** 28°F

## Problem Solving • Reasoning

**11.** Your normal body temperature is about 98°F. A cat's normal body temperature is 103°F. Is this above or below your body temperature?

_____

**12.** Water freezes at 32°F. The temperature was 6 degrees below freezing at noon on a January day. What was the temperature?

_____

Name _____    Date _____

# Problem-Solving Strategy: Work Backward

Sometimes in a problem you can start with what you know and work backward.

**Use the Work Backward strategy to solve each problem.**

1. Jill filled 3 1-quart containers. She had 1 pint left over. How many pints of milk did she start with?

   **Think:** What information should I start with?

   _____

2. Mark is going to empty several 1-cup containers into 1-pint containers. He fills 6 1-pint containers. How many 1-cup containers did he start with?

   **Think:** What information do I know?

   _____

**Solve. Use these and other strategies.**

### Problem-Solving Strategies

- Find a Pattern
- Work Backward
- Guess and Check

3. A third grade class visited a dairy farm. Each student received 1 cup of milk to drink. The class received a total of 14 pints of milk. How many were in the class?

   _____

4. Joe scoops milk from a large vat. He uses a 5-gallon pail. He needs to leave 15 gallons in the vat. He dips 5 times with the pail. How many gallons of milk were in the vat at the start?

   _____

5. Clare made a banner in 3 sections. The second section is 2 feet long. The third section is 24 inches long. The banner is 5 feet long. How long is the first section?

   _____

6. What is the next number in the pattern likely to be?

   3  4  6  9  13  18

   _____

Name _____ Date _____

# Centimeter and Decimeter

**Estimate. Then measure to the nearest centimeter.**

1  2  3  4  5  6  7  8  9  10
centimeters

**Example**

2 cm

1.

_____

2.

_____

3.

_____

4.

_____

5.

_____

**Choose the better estimate. Circle the answers.**

6. the length of your thumb

   **a.** 3 cm   **b.** 3 dm

7. the length of a fork

   **a.** 1 dm   **b.** 1 cm

8. the width of a glass

   **a.** 5 dm   **b.** 5 cm

## Problem Solving • Reasoning

9. Which is greater, a length of 2 decimeters or a length of 18 centimeters?

   _____

10. How many centimeters equal one and a half decimeters?

    _____

Name _____ Date _____

# Meter and Kilometer

| Example |
|---|
| length of a bicycle |
| m |

**Choose the unit you would use to measure each. Write *m* or *km*.**

**1.** distance across your state

_____

**2.** height of a flagpole

_____

**3.** height of a door

_____

**4.** the length of your classroom

_____

**5.** distance from Seattle, Washington to San Francisco, California

_____

**Choose the better estimate. Circle the answers.**

**6.** width of a window
  **a.** 1 km   **b.** 1 m

**7.** height of a bridge
  **a.** 10 m   **b.** 10 km

**8.** height of a teacher
  **a.** 2 m   **b.** 2 km

**Find the missing measure.**

**9.** 200 cm = _____ m

**10.** 4 km = _____ m

**11.** 30 m = _____ cm

**12.** 1 km = _____ m

**13.** 4 m = _____ dm

**14.** 20 km = _____ m

## Problem Solving • Reasoning

**15.** Jody runs a 3 km race. How many meters does she run?

_____

**16.** Bill has 3 m of rope. How many dm long is the rope? How many cm long is the rope?

_____

Name _____ Date _____

# Metric Units of Capacity

| Example |
|---|
| a cup of tea |
| mL |

**Choose the unit you would use to measure the capacity of each. Write *mL* or *L*.**

**1.** a juicebox

_____

**2.** gas tank of a car

_____

**3.** a teardrop

_____

**4.** fuel tank of an airplaine

_____

**5.** bowl of milk for a cat

_____

**Choose the better estimate. Circle the answers.**

**6.**

**a.** 150 L   **b.** 150 mL

**7.**

**a.** 5 L   **b.** 5 mL

**8.**

**a.** 10 L   **b.** 10 mL

**Find the missing measure.**

**9.** 2 L = _____ mL

**10.** 4,000 mL = _____ L

**11.** $\frac{1}{2}$ L = _____ mL

## Problem Solving • Reasoning

**12.** Victoria has a pitcher with 1,250 mL of water. She pours out 1 L. How much water is left in the pitcher?

_____

**13.** Aaron pours 3,000 mL of water into a kettle to make soup. Lois pours 4 L of water into the same kettle. How much water is in the kettle?

_____

Name _____ Date _____

# Problem-Solving Skill: Choose a Computation Method

**Solve. Choose mental math, estimation, or paper and pencil.**

1. Jordan visited famous buildings while he was on vacation. At one building he walked up 50 steps. Then he walked up 350 more steps to the top of the tower. How many steps did Jordan climb?

   **Think:** Are the numbers easy to add using mental math?

   _____

2. The zoo had 517 visitors on Monday and 391 visitors on Tuesday. About how many more people visited the zoo on Monday?

   **Think:** Do I need an exact answer or an estimate?

   _____

**Solve. Use these and other strategies.**

┌─────────────────────── **Problem-Solving Strategies** ───────────────────────┐

   • Find a Pattern          • Write a Number Sentence          • Work Backward

└──────────────────────────────────────────────────────────────────────────────┘

3. Joanne bought a new swimsuit and goggles. The swimsuit cost $29. The goggles cost $7. How much change did Joanne get from $40?

   _____

4. Kenan drove 13 miles on the first day of his vacation. The next day he drove 6 miles. The day after that he drove 26 miles. How many miles did Joe drive during the 3 days?

   _____

5. Jaran rode his bike for 1 mile on Monday morning. On Tuesday he rode for 3 miles. On Wednesday Jaran rode for 5 miles. If he continues with this pattern, how many miles will he likely ride on Friday?

   _____

6. Miguel filled his car with gas. He put 8 gallons of gas into the gas tank. Miguel figured that there had been 15 gallons of gas still in the tank before he filled it. How many gallons of gas does the tank hold?

   _____

Name _____ Date _____

# Metric Units of Mass

| Example |
|---|
| ping pong ball |
| g |

**Choose the unit you would choose to measure the mass of each. Write _g_ or _kg_.**

**1.** a cow

_____

**2.** a man

_____

**3.** piece of notebook paper

_____

**4.** a playing card

_____

**5.** a truck

_____

**Choose the better estimate. Circle the answers.**

**6.** a pig
 **a.** 350 kg **b.** 350 g

**7.** a sandal
 **a.** 4 kg **b.** 400 g

**8.** a dozen oranges
 **a.** 1 kg **b.** 10 g

**9.** a child
 **a.** 200 g **b.** 20 kg

**10.** a car
 **a.** 20 kg **b.** 800 kg

**11.** one apple
 **a.** 13 kg **b.** 130 g

**Find the missing measure.**

**12.** 2 kg = _____ g

**13.** 3,000 g = _____ kg

**14.** 6,000 g = _____ kg

**15.** 5 kg = _____ g

**16.** 7 kg = _____ g

**17.** 8,000 g = _____ kg

## Problem Solving • Reasoning

**18.** A basket of apples has a mass of 2 kg. Irene adds 570 g of apples to the basket. What is the mass of the basket of apples now?

_____

**19.** The mass of Martin's motor bike is 120 kg. He puts on a new set of rims that weighs 13 kg less than the old set. What is the mass of the bike now?

_____

Name _____ Date _____

# Temperature: Degrees Celsius

| Example |
|---|
| 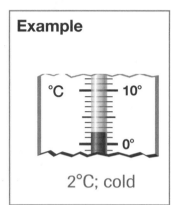 2°C; cold |

Write each temperature. Then write *hot, warm, cool,* or *cold* to describe the temperature.

**1.**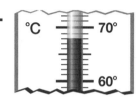

_____

**2.**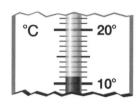

_____

**3.**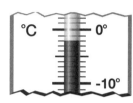

_____

**4.**

_____

**5.**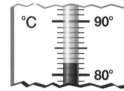

_____

**6.**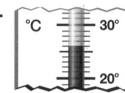

_____

**7.**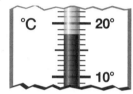

_____

Choose the better estimate of the temperature.
Circle the answers.

**8.**

**a.** 0°C    **b.** 25°C

**9.**

**a.** 10°C    **b.** 31°C

**10.**

**a.** 22°C    **b.** 70°C

## Problem Solving • Reasoning

**11.** Normal body temperature is 37°C. The water in a sink is 41°C. Is that above or below body temperature? By how many degrees?

_____

**12. Write About It** Describe an activity you might do outside if the temperature is −3°C.

_____

Name _____ Date _____

# Problem-Solving Application: Use Measurement

Remember:
► Understand
► Plan
► Solve
► Look Back

What you learned about measurement will help you solve some problems.

**Solve.**

1. Claudia manages a pet store. She uses 8 ounces of food for the gerbils every day. How many pounds of gerbil food does she use in 20 days?

   **Think:** How many ounces are in 1 pound?

   _____

2. The water in the fish tanks needs to be kept at 43 degrees above freezing on the Fahrenheit scale. What temperature should the water be?

   **Think:** What is the freezing point on the Fahrenheit scale?

   _____

**Solve. Use these and other strategies.**

---

**Problem-Solving Strategies**

- Draw a Picture
- Write a Number Sentence
- Guess and Check

---

3. Each kitten gets 200 mL of fresh water each day. Claudia has 6 kittens in the pet shop. How many liters of water do the kittens use in 5 days?

   _____

4. Claudia's puppy play yard measures 18 feet long. How many yards long is the play yard? How many inches long is the play yard?

   _____

5. Four students stand in a row. George, who is 59 inches tall, stands next to Linda. Bob, who is 5 feet 3 inches tall, is on the right end. Susan, who is 51 inches tall, and Linda, who is 4 feet 7 inches tall, stand in the two spaces at the left. How are the students ordered from left to right?

   _____

6. Seth used 16 half-inch slices of bread to make sandwiches for his friends. Now there are 12 half-inch slices of bread left in the package. How many inches long was the loaf of bread before Seth made the sandwiches?

   _____

Name _____    Date _____

# Modeling Multiplication

**Model with counters. Write an addition sentence and a multiplication sentence.**

---

**Example**

5 groups of 4

| **Model** | **Addition Sentence** | **Multiplication Sentence** |
|---|---|---|
| ★ ★ ★ ★<br>★ ★ ★ ★<br>★ ★ ★ ★<br>★ ★ ★ ★<br>★ ★ ★ ★ | $4 + 4 + 4 + 4 + 4 = 20$ | $5 \times 4 = 20$ |

---

**1.** 3 groups of 4

_____

_____

**2.** 4 groups of 6

_____

_____

**3.** 2 groups of 5

_____

_____

**4.** 6 groups of 3

_____

_____

**5.** 3 groups of 7

_____

_____

**6.** 5 groups of 3

_____

_____

**Write a multiplication sentence for each.**

**7.** $5 + 5 + 5 + 5 + 5 + 5 = 30$

_____

**8.** $4 + 4 + 4 + 4 + 4 + 4 + 4 + 4 = 32$

_____

## Problem Solving • Reasoning

**9.** Sara has 4 rows of stickers with 6 stickers in each row. How many stickers does she have?

_____

**10. Write About It** Can you write a multiplication sentence to go with this addition sentence? Explain why or why not.

$6 + 2 + 9 = 17$

_____

Name _____      Date _____

# Arrays and Multiplication

| Example |
|---|
| ★ ★ ★    ★ ★<br>★ ★ ★    ★ ★<br>              ★ ★<br><br>$2 \times 3 = 6$   $3 \times 2 = 6$ |

**Write a multiplication sentence for each array.**

1.

_____

2.

_____

3. X X X        X X X X<br>X X X        X X X X<br>X X X        X X X X<br>X X X

_____

4.

_____

5.

_____

## Problem Solving • Reasoning

6. Michael tapes the postcards people send him on a wall. So far he has 4 rows of 3 postcards. How many postcards does Michael have?

_____

7. There are 6 rows of 5 mailboxes at the post office. How many mailboxes are there?

_____

Name _____     Date _____

# Multiply With 2

| Example |
|---|
|  |
| $3 \times 2 = 6$ |

**Write a multiplication sentence for each picture.**

1.

_____

2.

_____

3.

_____

4.

_____

5.

_____

**Multiply.**

6.  $\begin{array}{r} 2 \\ \times 2 \\ \hline \end{array}$
7.  $\begin{array}{r} 4 \\ \times 2 \\ \hline \end{array}$
8.  $\begin{array}{r} 2 \\ \times 6 \\ \hline \end{array}$
9.  $\begin{array}{r} 7 \\ \times 2 \\ \hline \end{array}$
10. $\begin{array}{r} 5 \\ \times 2 \\ \hline \end{array}$
11. $\begin{array}{r} 2 \\ \times 3 \\ \hline \end{array}$

12. $\begin{array}{r} 9 \\ \times 2 \\ \hline \end{array}$
13. $\begin{array}{r} 2 \\ \times 8 \\ \hline \end{array}$
14. $\begin{array}{r} 6 \\ \times 2 \\ \hline \end{array}$
15. $\begin{array}{r} 10 \\ \times 2 \\ \hline \end{array}$
16. $\begin{array}{r} 2 \\ \times 5 \\ \hline \end{array}$
17. $\begin{array}{r} 2 \\ \times 4 \\ \hline \end{array}$

18. $3 \times 2$     19. $2 \times 5$     20. $2 \times 7$     21. $4 \times 2$     22. $8 \times 2$

_____     _____     _____     _____     _____

## Problem Solving • Reasoning

23. Mark has 6 chickens. Each of his chickens lays 2 eggs every day. How many eggs do all the chickens lay in one day?

24. Kim bought 4 puzzles. Each puzzle cost $2. How much did the puzzles cost altogether?

_____

Name _____    Date _____

# Multiply With 5

| Example |
|---|
| 4 |
| × 5 |
| 20 |

**Multiply.**

**1.**  5
    × 2

**2.**  5
    × 1

**3.**  3
    × 5

**4.**  5
    × 6

**5.**  7
    × 5

**6.**  6
    × 5

**7.**  5
    × 5

**8.**  8
    × 5

**9.**  5
    × 9

**10.**  1
    × 5

**11.**  2
    × 5

**12.**  5
    × 3

**13.**  9
    × 5

**14.**  5
    × 7

**15.**  5
    × 4

**16.**  5
    × 8

**17.**  5
    × 5

**18.** $5 \times 9$

**19.** $1 \times 5$

**20.** $4 \times 5$

**21.** $5 \times 6$

**22.** $5 \times 2$

**23.** $5 \times 3$

**24.** $8 \times 5$

**25.** $5 \times 5$

**26.** $5 \times 4$

**27.** $5 \times 7$

**28.** $5 \times 8$

**29.** $2 \times 5$

**30.** $5 \times 7$

**31.** $3 \times 5$

**32.** $6 \times 5$

## Problem Solving • Reasoning

**33.** Jane bought 6 boxes of cupcakes for a party. Each box has 5 cupcakes in it. How many cupcakes did Jane buy?

**34.** Kevin bought 5 packages of plastic cups for the party. Each package had 8 cups in it. How many cups did Kevin buy?

Name _____   Date _____

# Multiply With 10

| Example |
|---|
| 10 |
| $\times$ 5 |
| 10 |

**Find each product.**

**1.**  10
$\times$ 2

**2.**  6
$\times$ 10

**3.**  4
$\times$ 10

**4.**  3
$\times$ 10

**5.**  10
$\times$ 9

**6.**  10
$\times$ 1

**7.**  8
$\times$ 10

**8.**  10
$\times$ 7

**9.**  5
$\times$ 10

**10.**  10
$\times$ 6

**11.**  10
$\times$ 4

**12.**  10
$\times$ 6

**13.**  10
$\times$ 3

**14.**  9
$\times$ 10

**15.**  10
$\times$ 6

**16.**  7
$\times$ 10

**17.**  10
$\times$ 8

**18.** $10 \times 1$

**19.** $2 \times 10$

**20.** $6 \times 10$

**21.** $10 \times 5$

**22.** $10 \times 4$

_____   _____   _____   _____   _____

**23.** $10 \times 8$

**24.** $3 \times 10$

**25.** $10 \times 7$

**26.** $10 \times 9$

**27.** $10 \times 2$

_____   _____   _____   _____   _____

## Problem Solving • Reasoning

**28.** Bill reshelved videotapes in the school library. He put 10 videotapes on each shelf. Bill completely filled 5 shelves with videos. How many videos did Bill reshelve?

_____

**29.** Sherry opened a new box of pencils. There were 4 rows of pencils in the box. Each row had 10 pencils. How many pencils were in the box?

_____

Name _____  Date _____

# Problem-Solving Skill: Too Much Information

Problems sometimes give you more information than you need. You must decide which facts you need to solve the problem.

**Solve.**

**1.** The school library is getting new materials. Five new CD-ROMs costing $25 each arrived on Monday. Six new CD-ROMs costing $20 each arrived on Tuesday. How many new CD-ROMs did the library receive?

**Think:** What information is not needed?

_____

**2.** There will be 8 square tables in the new school library. There will also be 6 rectangular tables. Four chairs will fit at a square table. Six chairs will fit at a rectangular table. How many chairs will fit at the square tables?

**Think:** What information is not needed?

_____

**3.** Mr. Brandon used 4 movable shelves to carry books to the library. They cost $10 each. Each shelf holds 9 books. Four students each carry a movable shelf of books. How many books do they carry if each makes just one trip?

_____

**4.** The school is getting 2 new magazine subscriptions. *Treehouse* costs $3 a month. *National Photographic* costs $4 a month. How much does it cost for 3 months of *Treehouse?*

_____

**Solve. Use these and other strategies.**

### Problem-Solving Strategies

| • Act It Out | • Draw a Picture | • Use Logical Thinking |
|---|---|---|

**5.** There are 12 boys in Mr. Lauder's 3rd grade class. On Friday 3 boys were absent. How many boys were present in Mr. Lauder's class on Friday?

_____

**6.** Janet, Kathleen, and Linda each buy a new shirt. Kathleen's shirt has stars on it. Linda's shirt is striped. Who bought the plaid shirt?

_____

Name _____   Date _____

# Multiply With 1 and 0

| Example |
|---|
|  |
| $3 \times 1 = 3$ |

**Write a multiplication sentence for each picture.**

1.

2.

_____   _____

**Multiply.**

3.  8
    $\times 1$

4.  0
    $\times 6$

5.  5
    $\times 1$

6.  9
    $\times 1$

7.  4
    $\times 0$

8.  1
    $\times 1$

9.  1
    $\times 7$

10. 1
    $\times 2$

11. 3
    $\times 0$

12. 0
    $\times 5$

13. 6
    $\times 1$

14. 0
    $\times 9$

15. 1
    $\times 8$

16. 7
    $\times 0$

17. 1
    $\times 4$

18. 2
    $\times 1$

19. 1
    $\times 9$

20. 0
    $\times 8$

21. $10 \times 1$

22. $3 \times 0$

23. $1 \times 5$

24. $0 \times 10$

25. $8 \times 1$

_____   _____   _____   _____   _____

## Problem Solving • Reasoning

26. The teacher will give 1 prize to any student who completes the math test correctly. No one completed the test correctly. Write a number sentence to show how many prizes the teacher gave out.

_____

27. Ed had 3 songs to practice. He sang each song one time. How many songs did Ed sing in practice?

_____

Name _____     Date _____

# Multiply With 3

| Example |
|---|
| 3 |
| × 3 |
| 9 |

**Find each product.**

1.  3
    × 5

2.  9
    × 3

3.  5
    × 3

4.  1
    × 3

5.  7
    × 3

6.  6
    × 3

7.  3
    × 8

8.  3
    × 4

9.  0
    × 3

10. 3
    × 2

11. 10
    × 3

12. $3 \times 9$

13. $7 \times 3$

14. $3 \times 8$

15. $3 \times 3$

16. $4 \times 3$

_____   _____   _____   _____   _____

**Draw an array for each. Then complete each multiplication sentence.**

17. $3 \times 1$

18. $6 \times 3$

19. $9 \times 3$

20. $3 \times 5$

_____   _____   _____   _____

21. $3 \times 4$

22. $3 \times 0$

23. $2 \times 3$

24. $3 \times 10$

_____   _____   _____   _____

## Problem Solving • Reasoning

25. Jared is cleaning a large window. The window is divided into smaller squares. There are 3 squares across the top and 4 squares down the side. How many of these smaller squares does Jared clean?

_____

26. Lucia planted 3 rows of lettuce. Each row had 9 lettuce plants in it. How many lettuce plants did Lucia have in her garden?

_____

Name _____     Date _____

# Problem-Solving Strategy: Use Models to Act It Out

Remember:
► Understand
► Plan
► Solve
► Look Back

When you act out a problem, it will help you organize the information and you will be able to see the solution more easily.

**Solve.**

1. There are 8 students in Mrs. Cole's ballet class. Mrs. Cole brings 24 muffins. Shared equally, how many muffins does each student eat?

   **Think:** How could you use counters to act it out?

   _____

2. There are 20 students in Mrs. Cole's 10:00 A.M. class. If the students are placed in 4 equal groups, how many students are in each group?

   **Think:** How could you use counters to act it out?

   _____

3. At the start of the dance, five students stand on the left. Five students stand on the right. One student stands on the platform in the middle. How many students are in the dance?

   _____

4. Mrs. Cole's 1:00 P.M. class has 16 students. For the start of their recital dance, one student will stand to either side of the stage. The others will form 2 equal rows. How many students will be in each row?

   _____

**Solve. Use these and other strategies.**

| Problem-Solving Strategies |
| --- |
| • Act It Out    • Work Backward    • Find a Pattern |

5. Jeremy has a 12-foot board. He cuts a 5-foot piece from it. Then he cuts a 4-foot piece from what was left. How much is left of the original board?

   _____

6. A costume has a pattern of buttons. There are 3 buttons in the first row, then 6 buttons, 8 buttons, 11 buttons, and 13 buttons. How many buttons are in the sixth row?

   _____

Name _____ Date _____

# Multiply With 4

| Example |
|---|
| 5 |
| × 4 |
| 20 |

**Find each product.**

**1.** 4 × 7   **2.** 3 × 4   **3.** 8 × 4   **4.** 1 × 4   **5.** 4 × 2

**6.** 10 × 4   **7.** 6 × 4   **8.** 4 × 0   **9.** 7 × 4   **10.** 9 × 4   **11.** 4 × 1

**12.** 4 × 3   **13.** 4 × 8   **14.** 4 × 9   **15.** 2 × 4   **16.** 4 × 4   **17.** 4 × 5

**18.** 4 × 1   **19.** 6 × 4   **20.** 8 × 4   **21.** 3 × 4   **22.** 9 × 4

**23.** 5 × 4   **24.** 4 × 4   **25.** 7 × 4   **26.** 2 × 4   **27.** 4 × 10

## Problem Solving • Reasoning

**28.** Juliette had 4 cats. Each of the cats had a litter of 6 kittens. How many kittens did Juliette's cats have altogether?

**29.** Jim was hanging paintings in the hall for Parent's Night. In one section, Jim made an array that had 5 paintings across and 4 paintings down. How many paintings did Jim hang in this section?

Name _____     Date _____

# Problem-Solving Application: Use a Pictograph

You must analyze the information in a pictograph to help you solve the problem.

**Number of Trees in Hancock Park**

| Oak | 🌳🌳🌳🌳🌳🌳🌳🌳🌳 |
|---|---|
| Maple | 🌳🌳🌳🌳🌳 |
| Sweet gum | 🌳🌳🌳🌳🌳🌳🌳 |

Each 🌳 stands for 5 trees.

**Solve.**

**1.** Which kind of tree is most common in Hancock Park? How many of those trees are in the park?

**Think:** Which row has the most pictures?

_____

**2.** Which kind of tree is least common in Hancock Park? How many of those trees are in the park?

**Think:** Which row has the least number of pictures?

_____

**3.** How many more oaks than sweet gums are there in Hancock Park?

_____

**4.** How many maples and oaks are in Hancock Park?

_____

**Solve. Use these and other strategies.**

**Problem-Solving Strategies**

- Write a Number Sentence
- Work Backward
- Use Logical Thinking

**5.** Lucy and Charlie each bought a book for $3. Then Lucy bought a scarf for $5 and Charlie bought gloves for $6. How much money did Lucy spend?

_____

**6.** Charlene made 8 gallons of orange drink. She needed to put the orange drink into quart containers. How many containers will she need?

_____

Name _____ Date _____

# Using a Multiplication Table

| Example |
|---|
| 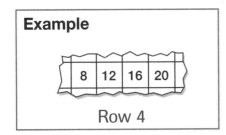 |
| Row 4 |

**In which row or column is each part of the multiplication table found?**

**1.**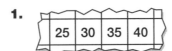

**2.**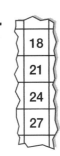

_____     _____

**3.**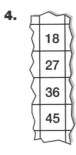

**4.**

**5.** 0 8 16

_____     _____     _____

## Problem Solving • Reasoning

**6.** Name the row in the multiplication table in which all the numbers end in a five or a zero.

_____

**7.** Name the column in the multiplication table that contains the number 49.

_____

Name _____  Date _____

# Multiply With 6

| Example |
|---|
| 8 |
| × 6 |
| 48 |

**Find each product.**

**1.**  4
  × 6

**2.**  5
  × 6

**3.**  1
  × 6

**4.**  6
  × 3

**5.**  6
  × 0

**6.**  7
  × 6

**7.**  9
  × 6

**8.**  2
  × 6

**9.**  6
  × 6

**10.**  6
  × 8

**11.**  6
  × 4

**12.**  6
  × 1

**13.**  0
  × 6

**14.**  6
  × 7

**15.**  6
  × 2

**16.**  6
  × 6

**17.**  6
  × 9

**18.** $3 \times 6$ _____

**19.** $6 \times 5$ _____

## Problem Solving • Reasoning

**20.** A camp has 6 volleyball games each day. How many games will be played in 5 days?

_____

**21.** There are 6 players on a volleyball team. How many players are there in a game between 2 teams?

_____

Name _____ Date _____

# Multiply With 8

| Example |
|---|
| 8 |
| $\times\ 8$ |
| 64 |

**Find each product.**

**1.**  6
   $\times\ 8$

**2.**  5
   $\times\ 8$

**3.**  1
   $\times\ 8$

**4.**  8
   $\times\ 3$

**5.**  8
   $\times\ 0$

**6.**  4
   $\times\ 8$

**7.**  9
   $\times\ 8$

**8.**  2
   $\times\ 8$

**9.**  8
   $\times\ 8$

**10.**  8
   $\times\ 5$

**11.**  8
   $\times\ 7$

**12.**  0
   $\times\ 8$

**13.**  4
   $\times\ 8$

**14.**  8
   $\times\ 1$

**15.**  8
   $\times\ 3$

**16.** $7 \times 8$ _____

**17.** $6 \times 8$ _____

**18.** $8 \times 2$ _____

**19.** $8 \times 9$ _____

## Problem Solving • Reasoning

**20.** Spiders have 8 legs. How many legs do 3 spiders have?

_____

**21.** Ants have 6 legs. Which have more legs, 3 spiders or 4 ants?

_____

Name _____  Date _____

# Problem-Solving Skill: Multistep Problems

Some problems require more than one step to solve.

**Solve.**

1. Allison is organizing 18 tapes in 3 boxes. Each box holds 8 tapes. How many more tapes fit in the boxes?

   **Think:** How many tapes can the 3 boxes hold?

   _____

2. Sue has 8 CDs. Kim has 7 more CDs than Sue. How many CDs do Sue and Kim have in all?

   **Think:** How many CDs does Kim have?

   _____

3. Bill is organizing his 23 tapes on 5 shelves. Each shelf holds 6 tapes. How many more tapes will fit on the shelves?

   _____

4. Molly has 6 CDs. Jean has 5 more CDs than Molly. How many CDs do Molly and Jean have together?

   _____

**Solve. Use these or other strategies.**

| Problem-Solving Strategies | | |
| --- | --- | --- |
| • Act It Out | • Write a Number Sentence | • Find a Pattern |

5. Two shelves hold 14 tapes. Three shelves hold 21 tapes. How many tapes will 4 shelves hold?

   _____

6. The product of 8 and a number is 56, What is 2 less than the number?

   _____

7. Three tapes last 6 hours. Four tapes last 8 hours. How long will 6 tapes last?

   _____

8. The sum of a number and 7 is 15. What is the product of the number and 4?

   _____

Name _____ Date _____

# Multiply With 7

| Example |
|---|
| 4 |
| × 7 |
| 28 |

**Find each product.**

**1.** 7 × 3

**2.** 7 × 6

**3.** 7 × 1

**4.** 5 × 7

**5.** 8 × 7

**6.** 7 × 2

**7.** 7 × 0

**8.** 7 × 7

**9.** 7 × 9

**10.** 4 × 7

**11.** 6 × 7

**12.** 7 × 3

**13.** 7 × 6

**14.** 0 × 7

**15.** 5 × 7

**16.** 8 × 7 _____

**17.** 2 × 7 _____

**18.** 7 × 9 _____

**19.** 7 × 7 _____

## Problem Solving • Reasoning

**20.** Tom's birthday is 4 weeks away. How many days away is Tom's birthday?

_____

**21.** Sue's school project is due in 5 weeks. How many days does Sue have to do it?

_____

Name _____   Date _____

# Multiply With 9

| Example |
|---|
| 6 |
| × 9 |
| 54 |

**Find each product.**

**1.** 　　4
　　× 9

**2.** 　　2
　　× 9

**3.** 　　7
　　× 9

**4.** 　　9
　　× 3

**5.** 　　9
　　× 8

**6.** 　　6
　　× 9

**7.** 　　9
　　× 9

**8.** 　　9
　　× 1

**9.** 　　9
　　× 0

**10.** 　　5
　　× 9

**11.** 　　8
　　× 9

**12.** $9 \times 2$ _____

**13.** $9 \times 5$ _____

**14.** $3 \times 9$ _____

**15.** $0 \times 9$ _____

**16.** $9 \times 1$ _____

**17.** $9 \times 9$ _____

**18.** $7 \times 9$ _____

**19.** $4 \times 9$ _____

## Problem Solving • Reasoning

**20.** There are 9 players on a baseball team. How many players are there on 8 teams?

_____

**21.** In a baseball game each team gets to bat 9 times. How many times does a team get to bat in 5 games?

_____

Name _____ Date _____

# Problem-Solving Strategy: Choose a Strategy

If there is more than one strategy that can be used to solve a problem, you need to decide which one to use.

**Solve.**

1. Graham bought three juggling balls and some wrapping paper for a present. He spent $10 in all. If the juggling balls cost $3 each, how much did Graham pay for the wrapping paper?

   **Think:** Which step should you do first to solve the problem?

   _____

2. Frank's plant is 2 inches taller than Sandy's plant. Carrie's plant is 5 inches shorter than Sandy's. Frank's plant is 12 inches tall. How tall is Carrie's plant?

   **Think:** How tall is Carrie's plant?

   _____

3. Jake had a box of video games. He gave three games each to Troy, Cori, Ethan, and Jackie. After giving these away, he had 4 games left over. How many games did he have at the beginning?

   _____

4. Marie brought home 6 dried flowers. She gave two of the flowers to her dad and the remainder to her brother and sister. Her brother received more flowers than her sister. How many flowers did Marie give to her sister?

   _____

**Solve. Use these or other strategies.**

**Problem-Solving Strategies**

| • Find a Pattern | • Act It Out | • Work Backward | • Guess and Check |

5. Gavin, Hamish, and Kelly are having a chess tournament. If each person plays each other two times, how many games will there be?

   _____

6. Greg and Dan bought candles at the craft fair. Greg bought 3 more candles than Dan. The total number of candles bought was 13. How many candles did Greg buy?

   _____

Name _____  Date _____

# Patterns on a Multiplication Table

| Example |
| --- |
| $6 \times \blacksquare = 18$ |
| 54 |

**Complete each multiplication sentence.**

**1.** $8 \times 9 = \blacksquare$

_____

**2.** $11 \times \blacksquare = 88$

_____

**3.** $\blacksquare \times 5 = 45$

_____

**4.** $6 \times \blacksquare = 36$

_____

**5.** $8 \times \blacksquare = 0$

_____

**6.** $7 \times 4 = \blacksquare$

_____

**7.** $\blacksquare \times 5 = 10$

_____

**8.** $\blacksquare \times 4 = 48$

_____

**9.** $3 \times \blacksquare = 21$

_____

**10.** $12 \times \blacksquare = 36$

_____

**11.** $11 \times \blacksquare = 11$

_____

**Write whether each array shows a square number.**

**12.** ■ ■ ■
■ ■ ■

_____

**13.** ■ ■ ■ ■
■ ■ ■ ■
■ ■ ■ ■
■ ■ ■ ■

_____

**14.** ■ ■ ■ ■ ■ ■
■ ■ ■ ■ ■ ■
■ ■ ■ ■ ■ ■
■ ■ ■ ■ ■ ■
■ ■ ■ ■ ■ ■

_____

## Problem Solving • Reasoning

**15.** Write three different multiplication sentences that have a product of 16.

_____

**16.** Is 121 a square number? Explain.

_____

_____

Name _____ Date _____

# Multiply Three Numbers

| Example |
|---|
| 6 × (4×2) |
| 6 × 8 |
| 48 |

**Find each product. Multiply the factors in parentheses first.**

**1.** 5 × (4 × 1)

_____

**2.** (3 × 2) × 7

_____

**3.** 6 × (3 × 2)

_____

**4.** 9 × (7 × 0)

_____

**5.** 8 × (7 × 1)

_____

**6.** 8 × (5 × 1)

_____

**7.** 2 × (3 × 4)

_____

**8.** 4 × (3 × 3)

_____

**9.** 8 × (0 × 3)

_____

**10.** 5 × (2 × 3)

_____

**11.** 7 × (1 × 5)

_____

**12.** (3 × 3) × 5

_____

**13.** (3 × 2) × 9

_____

**14.** 1 × (2 × 7)

_____

**15.** 7 × (2 × 2)

_____

**16.** 7 × (0 × 6)

_____

**17.** 7 × (1 × 7)

_____

**18.** (3 × 3) × 6

_____

**19.** 4 × (2 × 4)

_____

## Problem Solving • Reasoning

**20.** Anna, Ben, and Cindy each used 2 packs of poster paper. Each pack has 4 sheets of paper in it. How many sheets of paper did they use?

_____

**21.** Anna and Cindy are sisters. Their mother bought each girl 2 packs of hair bands. Each pack has 5 hair bands. How many hair bands did their mom buy?

_____

Name _____     Date _____

# Problem-Solving Application: Use Operations

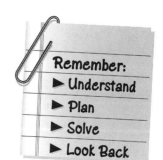

Remember:
► Understand
► Plan
► Solve
► Look Back

A combination of operations can be used to solve problems.

**Use the table to solve each problem.**

### Charity Cake Sale

|  | Price for 1 Slice | Price for Whole Cake |
|---|---|---|
| Carrot Cake | $2 | $9 |
| Coffee Cake | $1 | $8 |
| Sponge Cake | $3 | $10 |

**1.** Ms. Taylor bought 2 whole carrot cakes and a slice of sponge cake. How much did she spend?

**Think:** How much does 1 whole carrot cake cost?

_____

**2.** Ted bought 3 slices of sponge cake. Rosie bought a whole coffee cake. Who spent more money?

**Think:** How much did each spend?

_____

**Solve.**

### Problem-Solving Strategies

- Write a Number Sentence    • Work Backward    • Draw a Picture

**3.** After one hour, four whole carrot cakes, two whole coffee cakes, and one whole sponge cake had been sold. How much money was made?

_____

**4.** The cakes are in a row. The carrot cake is to the left of the sponge cake. The coffee cake is at the far right. Write the order of the cakes from left to right.

_____

**5.** Debbie bought a slice of carrot cake. She paid with quarters. How many quarters did she use?

_____

**6.** Sarah spent $32 on coffee cakes. How many whole coffee cakes did she buy?

_____

Name _____ Date _____

# Lines, Line Segments, Rays, and Angles

**Tell whether each figure is a *line, line segment,* or *ray.***

**Example:**
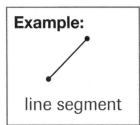
line segment

**1.**

_____

**2.**

_____

**3.**

_____

**4.**

_____

**5.**

_____

**6.**

_____

**7.**

_____

**Write *right angle, less than a right angle,* or *greater than a right angle* for each angle.**

**8.**

_____

**9.**

_____

**10.**

_____

**11.**

_____

**12.**

_____

**13.**

_____

**14.**

_____

**15.**

_____

## Problem Solving • Reasoning

**16.** What kind of angles are shown in the letter E?

_____

**17.** Can you find an example of a line in the real world? Explain.

_____

Name _____ Date _____

# Plane Figures

**Name each polygon.**

| Example | 1. | 2. | 3. |
|---|---|---|---|
|  pentagon |  _____ |  _____ |  _____ |

| 4. | 5. | 6. | 7. |
|---|---|---|---|
|  _____ |  _____ |  _____ |  _____ |

| 8. | 9. | 10. | 11. |
|---|---|---|---|
|  _____ |  _____ |  _____ |  _____ |

**Name the polygons that make up each shape.**

| 12. | 13. | 14. |
|---|---|---|
|  _____ |  _____ |  _____ |

## Problem Solving • Reasoning

**15.** Draw a figure that is not a polygon. Explain why it is not a polygon.

**16.** Is a circle a polygon? Explain.

_____        _____

Name _____   Date _____

# Quadrilaterals

**Tell if the figure is a quadrilateral. If it has a special name, write it.**

| Example | 1.  | 2.  | 3.  |
|---|---|---|---|
|  yes; rectangle | _____ | _____ | _____ |

4.

_____

5.

_____

6.

_____

7.

_____

8.

_____

9.

_____

10.

_____

11.

_____

12.

_____

13.

_____

14.

_____

15.

_____

16.

_____

17.

_____

18.

_____

19.

_____

## Problem Solving • Reasoning

**20.** How are squares and rectangles the same?

_____

**21.** How are squares and rectangles different?

_____

Name _____    Date _____

# Triangles

**Name the kind of triangle shown. Write *equilateral*, *isosceles*, or *right*.**

**Example**

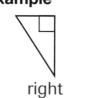

right

**1.**

_____

**2.**

_____

**3.**

_____

**4.**

_____

**5.**

_____

**6.**

_____

**7.**

_____

**8.**

_____

**9.**

_____

**10.**

_____

**11.**

_____

## Problem Solving

**12.** Suppose you draw a line connecting opposite corners of a sheet of paper. What kind of triangles would be formed?

_____

**13.** Draw a right triangle that is also an isosceles triangle.

_____

Name _____ Date _____

# Problem-Solving Skill: Visual Thinking

Sometimes you need to use visual thinking in order to solve problems.

**Circle the letter of the missing piece.**

**1.**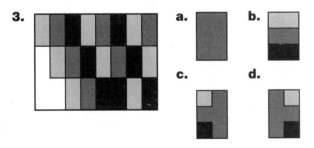

a.   b.

c.   d.

**Think:** Look at the rows in different ways to find the pattern.

**2.**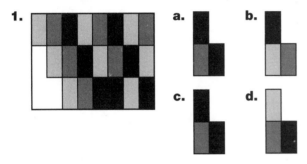

a.   b.

c.   d.

**Think:** Look at the rows in different ways to find the pattern.

**3.**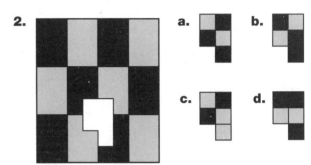

a.   b.

c.   d.

**Think:** Look at the rows in different ways to find the pattern.

**4.**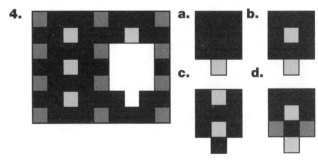

a.   b.

c.   d.

**Think:** Look at the rows in different ways to find the pattern.

**Solve. Use these or other strategies.**

$$\boxed{\text{Problem-Solving Strategies}}$$

| • Use Logical Thinking | • Find a Pattern | • Act it out | • Draw a Picture |

**5.** When Tom added 17 gallons of water to fill the vat, he knew that there must have been 15 gallons left before he filled it. How many gallons does the vat hold?

**6.** Josie planted 15 pansies in 3 rows. If there were an equal number of flowers in each row, how many pansies were there in one row?

Name _____    Date _____

# Congruent Figures

Trace one of the two figures. Place the traced figure on top
of the other figure. Are the figures in each pair congruent?

**Example**

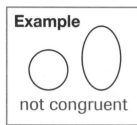

not congruent

**1.**

_____

**2.**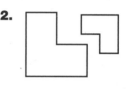

_____

**3.**

_____

**4.**

_____

**5.**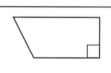

_____

Trace the first figure. Then choose the figure that is
congruent to it. Write *a, b,* or *c.*

**6.**

_____

| a. | b. | c. |
|----|----|----|
| 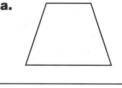 | 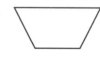 | 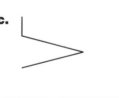 |

**7.**

_____

| a. | b. | c. |
|----|----|----|
|  | |  |

## Problem Solving • Reasoning

**8.** Suppose you drew a line connecting
opposite corners of a sheet of paper.
Would the triangles be congruent?
Explain.

_____

**9.** All squares have the same shape.
Are all squares congruent? Explain.

_____

Name _____  Date _____

# Line of Symmetry

**Tell whether each line appears to be a line of symmetry.**

**Example**

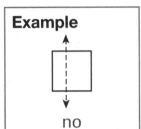

no

**1.**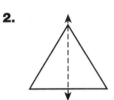

_____

**2.**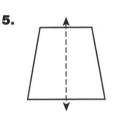

_____

**3.** 
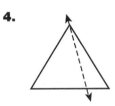

_____

**4.**

_____

**5.**

_____

**Draw a line of symmetry.**

**6.**

**7.**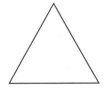

**8.**

## Problem Solving • Reasoning

**9.** Look at the triangle. How many lines of symmetry can you draw?

_____

**10.** Look at the square. How many lines of symmetry can you draw?

_____

Name _____ Date _____

# Perimeter

**Find each perimeter. Label your answer.**

**Example**

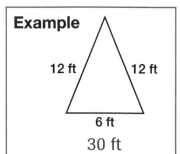

12 ft    12 ft

6 ft

30 ft

**1.**

8 ft

8 ft    8 ft

8 ft

_____

**2.**

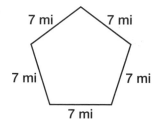

7 mi    7 mi

7 mi    7 mi

7 mi

_____

**3.**

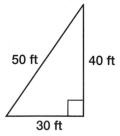

50 ft    40 ft

30 ft

_____

**4.**

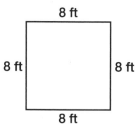

10 in.

20 in.    12 in.

12 in.

_____

**5.**

3 mi

6 mi    6 mi

3 mi

_____

**6.**

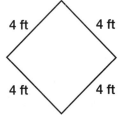

4 ft    4 ft

4 ft    4 ft

_____

**7.**

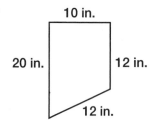

12 mi

5 mi

13 mi

_____

**8.**

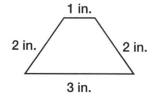

1 in.

2 in.    2 in.

3 in.

_____

## Problem Solving • Reasoning

**9.** The length of a side of an equilateral triangle is 5 inches. What is the perimeter?

_____

**10.** The length of a side of a square is 2 feet. What is the perimeter?

_____

Name _____  Date _____

# Estimating Area

**Example**

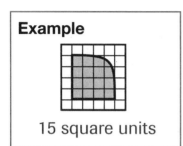

15 square units

The area of a figure is the number of square units needed to cover the figure. Count the number of square units inside the figure. Then look at the partly covered squares and estimate how many whole units they equal. The area of this figure is 15 square units.

**Estimate the area of each figure. Estimates may vary.**

**1.**

_____

**2.**

_____

**3.**
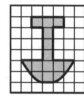

_____

**4.**

_____

**5.**

_____

**6.**

_____

**7.**

_____

**8.**

_____

**9.**

_____

Name _____    Date _____

# Find Area

**Find each area. Label your answer in square units.**

| | |
|---|---|
| **Example** <br>  <br> 9 square units | |

**1.**

_____

**2.**

_____

**3.**

_____

**4.**

_____

**5.**

_____

**6.**

_____

**7.**

_____

**Give an estimate of the area of each figure in square units. Estimates may vary.**

**8.**

_____

**9.**

_____

**10.**

_____

**11.**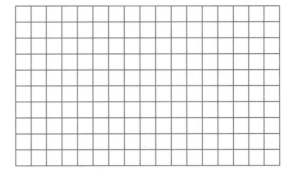

_____

## Problem Solving • Reasoning

**12.** Draw a rectangle with an area of 8 square units.

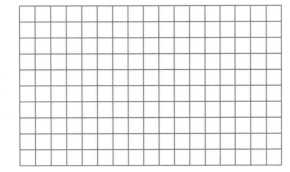

**13.** Draw an irregular figure with an area of 8 square units.

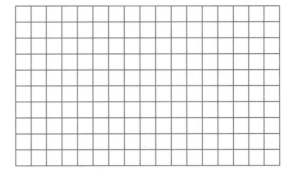

Name _____  Date _____

# Problem-Solving Strategy: Find a Pattern

Patterns include colors, figures, and shapes that repeat.

**Use the Find a Pattern strategy to solve each problem.**

**1.** Beth makes jewelry. She is stringing pink, pink, silver, gold, silver, pink, pink, silver, gold, silver, pink, pink, silver. If she continues the pattern, what colors will the next two beads be?

**Think:** How do the colors repeat?

_____

**2.** Beth is using beads of different shapes. The first 7 beads are round, square, oval, round, square, oval, round. If Beth continues this pattern, what are the shapes of the next two beads?

**Think:** How do the shapes repeat?

_____

**3.** For a pair of earrings, Beth is stringing silver, blue, red, blue, silver, blue, red, blue. If she continues this pattern, what will the color of the 12th bead be?

_____

**4.** Beth makes a sign for a craft fair with 20 stripes in this pattern: red, white, green, green, red, white, green, green. How many green stripes are there?

_____

**Solve. Use these or other strategies.**

> ### Problem-Solving Strategies
> 
> • Work Backward    • Find a Pattern    • Draw a Picture    • Act It Out

**5.** Hannah buys 2 necklaces at the craft fair for $15 each. What is her change from 2 twenty-dollar bills?

_____

**6.** Pete fills his lawn mower with 14 gallons of fuel. There are already 9 gallons in the tank. How much fuel does the tank hold?

_____

Name _____     Date _____

# Solid Figures

**Name the solid figure that each object looks like.**

| Example | |
|---|---|
| basketball | |

1.

_____

2.

_____

3.

_____

4.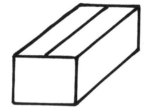

_____

5.

_____

6.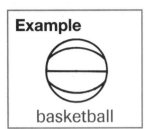

_____

7.

_____

## Problem Solving • Reasoning

**8.** Which solid figure has only 1 face?

_____

**9.** Which solid figure has no faces and no vertices?

_____

Name _____  Date _____

# Estimating Volume

The number of cubes that make up a solid figure is the **volume.**

- Find a container. It can be something in your classroom, such as a box or a pencil cup.

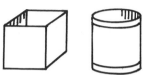

- Estimate the volume of the container. Record your estimate.

- Use the unit cubes to fill your container. Record how many cubes you use.

- Is your estimate close to the actual number of cubes you used to fill the container?

**Choose other containers. Estimate how many cubes it will take to fill each container. Record your estimates and then use unit cubes to fill the containers. Record the number of cubes you use.**

|    | Container | Estimate | Number of Cubes Used |
|----|-----------|----------|----------------------|
| 1. |           |          |                      |
| 2. |           |          |                      |
| 3. |           |          |                      |

## Problem Solving • Reasoning

4. Fill a pencil cup with cubes. Is the actual volume greater than, less than, or equal to the number of cubes used to fill the cup?

5. Draw two different solid figures that have the same volume.

_____

_____

Name _____    Date _____

# Find Volume

**Find the volume of each figure.**

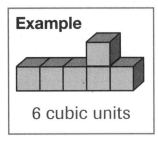

**Example**

6 cubic units

**1.**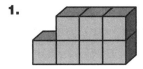

_____

**2.**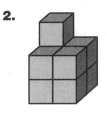

_____

**3.**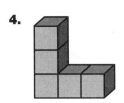

_____

**4.**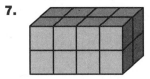

_____

**5.**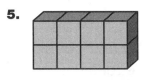

_____

**6.**

_____

**7.**

_____

**8.**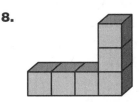

_____

## Problem Solving • Reasoning

**9.** Suppose you fill a rectangular box with 9 unit cubes. What is one arrangement of 9 unit cubes that would fill a box? Use unit cubes to support your answer.

_____

**10.** Now you fill another rectangular box with 12 unit cubes. What is one arrangement of 12 unit cubes that would fill a box? Use unit cubes to support your answer.

_____

Name _____ Date _____

# Problem-Solving Application: Use Measurement

Remember:
► Understand
► Plan
► Solve
► Look Back

Use what you learned about area, perimeter, and volume to solve problems.

**Solve. Find the perimeter, area, or volume.**

**1.** Drew is planning a garden. He wants to put a border around it. How much border does he need to go around the garden?

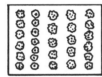

**Think:** Do I need to find the perimeter, area, or volume?

_____

**2.** Alice is planning a vegetable garden. She makes a model to plan what she wants to grow. What is the area of the model?

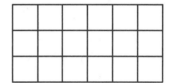

**Think:** How do I find area?

_____

**Solve. Use these or other strategies.**

┌─────────────── **Problem-Solving Strategies** ───────────────┐

• Find a Pattern   • Draw a Picture   • Use Logical Thinking   • Write a Number Sentence

**3.** Alice wants to put a fence around her garden. Should she find the area, perimeter, or volume of the garden? Why?

_____

**4.** Alice plants vegetable rows in the following pattern: peppers, tomatoes, carrots, peppers, tomatoes, carrots. What will she plant in the next two rows?

_____

**5.** The numbers 1, 4, 7, 10, 13 form a pattern. Whis is the next number in the pattern likely to be?

_____

**6.** Alice is twice as old as Bob. In 5 years Alice will be 15. How old is Bob now?

_____

Name _____ Date _____

# Modeling Division

Find the number in each equal group. Then complete each division sentence. Use the space beside the box to show your work.

| | Total Number | Number of Equal Groups | Number in Each Group | Division Sentence |
|---|---|---|---|---|
| Example | 8 | 4 | 2 | 8 ÷ 4 = 2 |
| 1. | 15 | 3 | | 15 ÷ 3 = _____ |
| 2. | 20 | 4 | | 20 ÷ 4 = _____ |

Write a division sentence to describe each picture.

3.

_____

4.

_____

## Problem Solving • Reasoning

5. **Write About It** You have two $10 bills and two $5 bills. If you divide the total into 2 equal groups, how much is in each group? Explain how you found your answer.

_____

6. You have one $20 bill. Explain how you could divide the $20 into 5 equal groups. Write a division sentence to show how this could be done.

_____

Name _____ Date _____

# Relate Multiplication and Division

| Example |
| --- |

$$5 \times 3 = 15$$
$$3 \times 5 = 15$$
$$15 \div 5 = 3$$
$$15 \div 3 = 5$$

**Write a multiplication sentence and a division sentence for each array.**

1.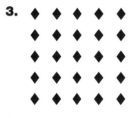

   _____    _____

2. ★ ★ ★ ★ ★ ★
   ★ ★ ★ ★ ★ ★
   ★ ★ ★ ★ ★ ★
   ★ ★ ★ ★ ★ ★

3. ◆ ◆ ◆ ◆ ◆
   ◆ ◆ ◆ ◆ ◆
   ◆ ◆ ◆ ◆ ◆
   ◆ ◆ ◆ ◆ ◆
   ◆ ◆ ◆ ◆ ◆

   _____    _____    _____    _____

**Draw an array for each multiplication sentence. Then write two related division sentences.**

4. $2 \times 4 = 8$    5. $3 \times 7 = 21$    6. $4 \times 8 = 32$    7. $6 \times 1 = 6$

   _____    _____    _____    _____

## Problem Solving • Reasoning

8. Write a multiplication sentence to find the total number of desks in the classroom. There are 6 rows in the classroom. Each row has 5 desks. How many people in all can sit in the 6 rows?

   _____

9. There are 27 people sitting in 3 equal rows. Write a division sentence to show how many people are in each row.

   _____

**Use with text pages 356–358.** **93**

Name _____   Date _____

# Divide by 2

| Example |
|---|
| $2 \times 2 = 4$ |
| $4 \div 2 = 2$ |

**Use the related multiplication fact to find each quotient.**

**1.** $2 \times 3 = 6$      **2.** $2 \times 1 = 2$      **3.** $2 \times 6 = 12$

   $6 \div 2 =$ _____      $2 \div 2 =$ _____      $12 \div 2 =$ _____

**4.** $2 \times 5 = 10$   **5.** $2 \times 7 = 14$   **6.** $2 \times 4 = 8$   **7.** $2 \times 9 = 18$

   $10 \div 2 =$ _____   $14 \div 2 =$ _____   $8 \div 2 =$ _____   $18 \div 2 =$ _____

**Divide.**

**8.** $8 \div 2$   **9.** $12 \div 2$   **10.** $10 \div 2$   **11.** $16 \div 2$   **12.** $2 \div 2$

_____   _____   _____   _____   _____

**13.** $6 \div 2$   **14.** $4 \div 2$   **15.** $14 \div 2$   **16.** $18 \div 2$   **17.** $20 \div 2$

_____   _____   _____   _____   _____

**Problem Solving • Reasoning**

**18.** In the band there are 8 majorettes. When they march, each row will have 2 majorettes. How many rows of majorettes will there be?

_____

**19.** The band director has 18 tuba players. He asks them to stand in 2 rows. How many tuba players will be in each row?

_____

Name _____ Date _____

# Divide by 5

| Example |
|---|
| $5 \times n = 15$ |
| $15 \div 5 = n$ |
| $n = 3$ |

**Find the missing factor. Then find the quotient.**

**1.** $5 \times n = 30$  **2.** $5 \times n = 5$  **3.** $5 \times n = 20$  **4.** $5 \times n = 40$

$30 \div 5 = n$   $5 \div 5 = n$   $20 \div 5 = n$   $40 \div 5 = n$

_____   _____   _____   _____

**5.** $5 \times n = 10$  **6.** $5 \times n = 35$  **7.** $5 \times n = 45$  **8.** $5 \times n = 25$  **9.** $5 \times n = 50$

$10 \div 5 = n$   $35 \div 5 = n$   $45 \div 5 = n$   $25 \div 5 = n$   $50 \div 5 = n$

_____   _____   _____   _____   _____

**Divide.**

**10.** $35 \div 5$  **11.** $30 \div 5$  **12.** $10 \div 5$  **13.** $25 \div 5$  **14.** $5 \div 5$

_____   _____   _____   _____   _____

**15.** $6 \div 2$  **16.** $15 \div 5$  **17.** $16 \div 2$  **18.** $40 \div 5$  **19.** $20 \div 2$

_____   _____   _____   _____   _____

**20.** $20 \div 5$  **21.** $10 \div 5$  **22.** $45 \div 5$  **23.** $12 \div 2$  **24.** $30 \div 5$

_____   _____   _____   _____   _____

## Problem Solving • Reasoning

**25.** Mrs. Scott's class has 25 students. She wants to make 5 equal rows of desks for her students. How many desks will be in each row?

**26.** The art teacher has 35 pounds of clay. If each student gets 5 pounds of clay, how many students are there?

_____   _____

Name _____     Date _____

# Problem-Solving Skill: Choose the Operation

Sometimes you need to decide whether to add, subtract, multiply, or divide to solve a problem.

**Solve.**

1. The third grade is holding a fair. They want to have 10 booths. Each booth needs 5 students to operate. How many students will be needed to operate 5 booths?

   **Think:** Do you need to find a total amount?

   _____

2. Mr. Wilson's class has 15 students. They want to make 5 game booths. How many students can they put at each game booth if they want the same number of students at each booth?

   **Think:** Do you need to find equal groups?

   _____

3. The Parent Committee sends in 20 prizes on Tuesday, 16 prizes on Wednesday, and 32 prizes on Thursday. How many prizes did the committee send in all?

   _____

4. Last year the school fair gave away 306 prizes. This year there were 378 prizes given away at the school fair. How many more prizes were given away this year?

   _____

**Solve. Use these or other strategies.**

╔══════════ **Problem-Solving Strategies** ══════════╗
- Write a Number Sentence     • Guess and Check     • Work Backward     • Draw a Picture

5. Mrs. Johnston's class wants to give out 5 prizes each hour in a prize drawing. They have 35 prizes to give away. How many times can they hold a drawing?

   _____

6. At the balloon game, each player gets 3 darts to throw. Draw a picture to show how many darts are needed if 5 students play at the same time.

   _____

Name _____ Date _____

# Division Rules

| Example |
|---------|
| 5 ÷ 1 = 5 |

**Divide.**

**1.** 0 ÷ 2 _____

**2.** 4 ÷ 4 _____

**3.** 0 ÷ 1 _____

**4.** 0 ÷ 5 _____

**5.** 9 ÷ 1 _____

**6.** 7 ÷ 7 _____

**7.** 7 ÷ 1 _____

**8.** 5 ÷ 5 _____

**9.** 2 ÷ 1 _____

**10.** 0 ÷ 8 _____

**11.** 6 ÷ 1 _____

**12.** 0 ÷ 4 _____

**13.** 1 ÷ 1 _____

**14.** 0 ÷ 9 _____

**Complete each table.**

**Rule: Divide by 1**

| | Input | Output |
|---|---|---|
| **15.** | 2 | _____ |
| **16.** | 4 | _____ |
| **17.** | _____ | 6 |
| **18.** | 8 | _____ |
| **19.** | _____ | 9 |

**Rule: Divide by 5**

| | Input | Output |
|---|---|---|
| **20.** | 10 | _____ |
| **21.** | 25 | _____ |
| **22.** | _____ | 6 |
| **23.** | 45 | _____ |
| **24.** | _____ | 10 |

## Problem Solving • Reasoning

**25.** Sally has 25 marbles. She wants to give one to each person she meets. To how many people can she give a marble?

_____

**26.** There are 9 children in art class. The art teacher gives them no colored pencils. How many colored pencils do the children have?

_____

Name _____  Date _____

# Divide by 3

| Example |
|---|
| 3 |
| 3)9 |

**Divide.**

**1.**
3)6

**2.**
3)18

**3.**
3)12

**4.**
3)30

**5.**
3)12

**6.**
3)18

**7.**
3)27

**8.**
3)21

**9.**
3)0

**10.** $3 \div 3$

**11.** $6 \div 3$

**12.** $12 \div 3$

**13.** $18 \div 3$

**14.** $9 \div 3$

_____    _____    _____    _____    _____

**15.** $24 \div 3$

**16.** $15 \div 3$

**17.** $21 \div 3$

**18.** $30 \div 3$

**19.** $27 \div 3$

_____    _____    _____    _____    _____

**Compare. Write >, <, or = for each ◯.**

**20.** $12 \div 3 \bigcirc 9 \div 3$

**21.** $15 \div 3 \bigcirc 18 \div 3$

**22.** $27 \div 3 \bigcirc 21 \div 3$

**23.** $15 \div 5 \bigcirc 15 \div 3$

**24.** $30 \div 3 \bigcirc 30 \div 5$

**25.** $12 \div 2 \bigcirc 12 \div 3$

## Problem Solving • Reasoning

**26.** Mary wants to make 3 rows of flowers in her garden. She has 18 packs of seeds. If she uses the same number of packs for each row, how many packs will she need for each row?

_____

**27.** Walter has 9 feet of lumber. How How many yards of lumber does Walter have?

_____

Name _____ Date _____

# Problem-Solving Strategy: Draw a Picture

Sometimes you can solve a problem by drawing a picture.

**Solve.**

1. Angela is sewing. Her dress pattern calls for 4 yards of red cloth. Angela wants to make 3 dresses. How many yards of red cloth will she need?

   **Think:** How can you show the yards of cloth?

   _____

2. Albert is making clay flower pots. He needs 2 pounds of clay for each pot. Albert wants to make 5 flowerpots. How many pounds of clay will he need?

   **Think:** How can you show the pounds of clay?

   _____

**Solve. Use these or other strategies.**

| Problem-Solving Strategies |
| --- |
| • Find a Pattern   • Write a Number Sentence   • Work Backward   • Draw a Picture |

3. The art teacher designs a rug pattern. One rug will need 3 pieces of orange yarn. She cuts 24 pieces of orange yarn. How many rugs can she make?

   _____

4. The rug pattern also calls for 10 pieces of yellow yarn. If the art teacher wants to make 5 rugs, how much yarn will she need?

   _____

5. The art teacher has 24 inches of red yarn. She wants to include an equal piece of red yarn in each of 8 rugs. How long will each piece be?

   _____

6. The art teacher has one piece of yarn that is 50 inches long. She cuts it in half. Then she cuts each half into 5 equal pieces. How much yarn does she have? How long is each piece?

   _____

Name _____     Date _____

# Divide by 4

| Example |
|---|
| $\begin{array}{r} 6 \\ 4\overline{)24} \end{array}$ |

**Find the quotient.**

**1.**  $4\overline{)8}$     **2.**  $4\overline{)20}$     **3.**  $4\overline{)36}$     **4.**  $4\overline{)40}$

**5.**  $4\overline{)12}$     **6.**  $4\overline{)16}$     **7.**  $4\overline{)28}$     **8.**  $4\overline{)32}$     **9.**  $4\overline{)4}$

**10.** $4 \div 4$     **11.** $16 \div 4$     **12.** $12 \div 4$     **13.** $28 \div 4$     **14.** $32 \div 4$

_____     _____     _____     _____     _____

**15.** $24 \div 4$     **16.** $20 \div 4$     **17.** $32 \div 4$     **18.** $40 \div 4$     **19.** $36 \div 4$

_____     _____     _____     _____     _____

## Problem Solving • Reasoning

**20.** There are 36 girls at a gymnastics meet. Only a group of 4 girls can compete at the same time. If each group takes 1 hour to compete, how long will it take 36 girls to compete?

_____

**21.** There are 4 gymnastics meets on the same Saturday. The coach can send 4 boys to each meet. How many boys can she send to the gymnastics meets in all?

_____

Name _____  Date _____

# Problem-Solving Application: Find Unit Cost

Remember:
► Understand
► Plan
► Solve
► Look Back

The cost of a single item is called the unit cost. You can divide to find the cost of a single item.

**Find the unit cost to solve each problem.**

**1.** The school cook is planning lunch. To make 10 sandwiches, she will need 1 pound of bread. She can get a 1-pound loaf of bread for $1. How much will the cook spend on bread if she makes 30 sandwiches?

**Think:** What is the cost for 1 pound of bread? How many pounds of bread will the cook need?

_____

**2.** There are 6 carrots in a bunch. Each bunch costs $2. Molly makes 6 carrot cakes. She needs 2 carrots for each cake. How much will Molly spend for carrots to make her cakes?

**Think:** What is the cost of 1 bunch of carrots? How many bunches of carrots will Molly need?

_____

**Solve. Use these or other strategies.**

### Problem-Solving Strategies

• Write a Number Sentence  • Work Backward  • Guess and Check  • Use Logical Thinking

**3.** Tanya wants to buy a slice of apple pie. A whole pie costs $12. There are 6 slices in a whole pie. How much will Tanya have to pay for one slice?

_____

**4.** Sally made $24 selling peach pies. Each pie was divided into 6 slices. Each slice cost $1. How many total pies did she sell?

_____

**5.** A half-pound of ham will make 2 sandwiches. The school cook pays $3 a pound for ham. She spends $18. How many sandwiches did she make?

_____

**6.** A loaf of bread has 24 slices and costs $2. Each sandwich has 2 slices. How many loaves does the cook need to make 24 sandwiches? How much will it cost in all?

_____

Name _____     Date _____

# Using a Multiplication Table to Divide

A multiplication table can also help you to divide.

The numbers in the rows are the **divisors.**
Move across the rows to find the **dividends.**
The numbers at the top of the columns are the
**quotients.**

**Example**

| × | 0 | 1 | 2 | 3 | 4 | 5 | 6 | 7 | 8 | 9 | 10 |
|---|---|---|---|---|---|---|---|---|---|---|----|
| 0 | 0 | 0 | 0 | 0 | 0 | 0 | 0 | 0 | 0 | 0 | 0 |
| 1 | 0 | 1 | 2 | 3 | 4 | 5 | 6 | 7 | 8 | 9 | 10 |
| 2 | 0 | 2 | 4 | 6 | 8 | 10 | 12 | 14 | 16 | 18 | 20 |
| 3 | 0 | 3 | 6 | 9 | 12 | 15 | 18 | 21 | 24 | 27 | 30 |
| 4 | 0 | 4 | 8 | 12 | 16 | 20 | 24 | 28 | 32 | 36 | 40 |
| 5 | 0 | 5 | 10 | 15 | 20 | 25 | 30 | 35 | 40 | 45 | 50 |
| 6 | 0 | 6 | 12 | 18 | 24 | 30 | 36 | 42 | 48 | 54 | 60 |
| 7 | 0 | 7 | 14 | 21 | 28 | 35 | 42 | 49 | 56 | 63 | 70 |
| 8 | 0 | 8 | 16 | 24 | 32 | 40 | 48 | 56 | 64 | 72 | 80 |
| 9 | 0 | 9 | 18 | 27 | 36 | 45 | 54 | 63 | 72 | 81 | 90 |
| 10 | 0 | 10 | 20 | 30 | 40 | 50 | 60 | 70 | 80 | 90 | 100 |

$$56 \div 8 = 7$$

**Use the multiplication table to complete the chart. The first one is done for you.**

| Problem | Divisor | Dividend | Quotient |
|---------|---------|----------|----------|
| $25 \div 5$ | 5 | 25 | 5 |
| **1.** $42 \div 6$ | _____ | _____ | _____ |
| **2.** $81 \div 9$ | _____ | _____ | _____ |
| **3.** $36 \div 6$ | _____ | _____ | _____ |
| **4.** $35 \div 5$ | _____ | _____ | _____ |
| **5.** $48 \div 6$ | _____ | _____ | _____ |
| **6.** $27 \div 3$ | _____ | _____ | _____ |
| **7.** $14 \div 2$ | _____ | _____ | _____ |

## Problem Solving • Reasoning

**8.** Doug buys 48 baseball cards. The cards came in 8 packages. How many cards came in each package?

_____

**9.** Denise recorded 15 songs onto 5 tapes. Each tape has the same number of songs. How many songs are on each tape?

_____

Name _____  Date _____

# Fact Families

**Complete each fact family.**

| **Example** | $4 \times 5 = 20$ |
| --- | --- |
| | $5 \times 4 = 20$ |
| | $20 \div 4 = 5$ |
| | $20 \div 5 = 4$ |

**1.** $3 \times 2 = 6$

$2 \times$ _____ $= 6$

$6 \div 3 =$ _____

$6 \div$ _____ $= 3$

**2.** $4 \times 9 = 36$

$9 \times 4 =$ _____

$36 \div 4 =$ _____

$36 \div$ _____ $= 4$

**Write a fact family for each array.**

**3.**

_____

_____

_____

_____

**4.**

_____

_____

_____

_____

## Problem Solving • Reasoning

**5.** Jenna wants to arrange her button collection in a display case. She has 45 buttons. Write two ways she could display her buttons in equal rows.

_____

**6** Which collection has more shells, 9 rows of 4 shells, or 7 rows of 5 shells?

_____

Name _____     Date _____

# Divide by 10

**Divide.**

| Example          5 |
|---|
| 10)50 |

**1.** 10)‾70‾

**2.** 10)‾30‾

**3.** 10)‾10‾

**4.** 10)‾60‾

**5.** 10)‾20‾

**6.** 10)‾100‾

**7.** 10)‾80‾

**8.** 10)‾90‾

**9.** 10)‾40‾

**10.** 80 ÷ 10

**11.** 30 ÷ 10

**12.** 0 ÷ 10

**13.** 50 ÷ 10

**14.** 20 ÷ 10

_____  _____  _____  _____  _____

**15.** 90 ÷ 10

**16.** 40 ÷ 10

**17.** 80 ÷ 10

**18.** 70 ÷ 10

**19.** 60 ÷ 10

_____  _____  _____  _____  _____

**Find each missing number.**

**20.** $10 \times$ _____ $= 20$

**21.** $40 \div$ _____ $= 4$

**22.** _____ $\times 10 = 70$

**23.** _____ $\div 10 = 8$

**24.** _____ $\times 4 = 40$

**25.** $5 \times 10 =$ _____

**26.** $10 \times$ _____ $= 60$

**27.** _____ $\times 10 = 30$

## Problem Solving • Reasoning

**28.** Carla bought 40 cans of beans for the picnic. She put 10 cans in each bag. How many bags did she fill?

_____

**29.** Ben packed 60 oranges in a crate. He packed 10 oranges in each row. How many rows did he make?

_____

Name _____    Date _____

# Problem-Solving Skill:
# Too Much or Too Little Information

If there is too much information in a problem, you need to decide which facts to use. If there is not enough information, you need to decide what information is missing.

| Bakery Prices | |
|---|---|
| Roll | 10¢ |
| Bread | |
| large loaf | $3 |
| small loaf | $2 |

**Solve. If not enough information is given, tell what information is needed to solve the problem.**

1. On Monday, David spends 60¢ on rolls. How many does he buy?

   **Think:** There is more information than you need to solve the problem.

   _____

2. Ellie buys 2 loaves of bread. How much money does she owe Harry?

   **Think:** Do you know the sizes of the loaves that Ellie buys?

   _____

3. Frances buys 3 large loaves of bread and 5 bagels. How much does she spend?

   _____

4. Kevin buys 2 small loaves of bread. He gives Harry $5. What is his change?

   _____

**Solve. Use these or other strategies.**

### Problem-Solving Strategies

• Draw a Picture    • Guess and Check    • Write a Number Sentence    • Work Backward

5. Harry arranges 3 rows of bread. Each row has 5 loaves. How many loaves of bread does he use?

   _____

6. Harry has two bags of flour that weigh 52 pounds. One bag weighs 8 pounds more than the other. How much does each bag weigh?

   _____

Name _____    Date _____

# Divide by 6

**Find each quotient.**

| Example $\dfrac{3}{6)18}$ | **1.** $6)\overline{6}$ | **2.** $6)\overline{24}$ | **3.** $6)\overline{42}$ | **4.** $6)\overline{12}$ |
|---|---|---|---|---|

**5.** $6)\overline{54}$     **6.** $6)\overline{60}$     **7.** $6)\overline{48}$     **8.** $6)\overline{36}$     **9.** $6)\overline{30}$

**10.** $54 \div 6$    **11.** $18 \div 6$    **12.** $30 \div 6$    **13.** $42 \div 6$    **14.** $6 \div 6$

_____  _____  _____  _____  _____

**15.** $48 \div 6$    **16.** $36 \div 6$    **17.** $12 \div 6$    **18.** $24 \div 6$    **19.** $60 \div 6$

_____  _____  _____  _____  _____

## Problem Solving • Reasoning

**20.** Larry is planting tomatoes in rows of 6. He buys 54 tomato plants at the garden store. How many rows of tomatoes will Larry plant?

_____

**21.** Rachel has 25 gardening books to display for the library. If she puts books in rows of 6, will each row have the same number of books?

_____

**22.** Louise plants 18 pepper plants in rows of 6. How many rows does she plant?

_____

**23.** James works for 6 hours a day in his garden during his vacation. He works a total of 24 hours. How many days does he work?

_____

Name _____     Date _____

# Divide by 7

**Divide.**

| Example     10 | **1.** | **2.** | **3.** | **4.** |
|---|---|---|---|---|
| $7\overline{)70}$ | $7\overline{)14}$ | $7\overline{)35}$ | $7\overline{)7}$ | $7\overline{)42}$ |

**5.**
$7\overline{)56}$

**6.**
$7\overline{)21}$

**7.**
$7\overline{)63}$

**8.**
$7\overline{)28}$

**9.**
$7\overline{)49}$

**10.** $28 \div 7$

**11.** $63 \div 7$

**12.** $35 \div 7$

**13.** $42 \div 7$

**14.** $7 \div 7$

_____ _____ _____ _____ _____

**15.** $49 \div 7$

**16.** $14 \div 7$

**17.** $56 \div 7$

**18.** $21 \div 7$

**19.** $70 \div 7$

_____ _____ _____ _____ _____

## Problem Solving • Reasoning

**20.** Alicia has 42 postcards. She puts 7 postcards on each page of her photo book. How many pages does she use?

_____

**21.** Zak hiked 70 miles during his vacation. He hiked the same number of miles each day for 7 days. How many miles did he hike each day?

_____

**22.** Gus works for 35 hours at the camp. He works 7 hours a day. How many days does he work?

_____

**23.** Annie bikes for 14 miles. She bikes 7 miles each day. How many days does she bike?

_____

Name _____   Date _____

# Problem-Solving Strategy: Write a Number Sentence

Remember:
► Understand
► Plan
► Solve
► Look Back

Sometimes you can write a number sentence to solve a problem.

**Solve the problems using the Number Sentence strategy.**

1. Kelly School is getting ready for the school play. Mrs. Pollard asks Bob to set up 24 more chairs. Bob puts 6 chairs in each row. How many rows does he make?

   **Think:** What operation can help you find the number of equal groups?

   _____

2. Carol has play programs to give to 10 ushers. Each usher gets 9 programs How many programs does Carol have?

   **Think:** How can you find the total when there are equal groups?

   _____

3. Ted is in charge of lighting. There are 18 lights that are connected to 3 switches. The same number of lights is on each switch. How many lights are on each switch?

   _____

4. Alice is giving balloons to the performers in the play. Each actor will get 4 balloons. There are 8 actors in the play. How many balloons does Alice need?

   _____

**Solve. Use these or other strategies.**

### Problem-Solving Strategies

| • Write a Number Sentence | • Draw a Picture | • Find a Pattern | • Guess and Check |
|---|---|---|---|

5. Corey has 18 tickets to sell. He takes 6 more to sell. Then he sells 12 tickets. How many tickets does he have now?

   _____

6. Linda hangs lights. The first 7 lights are green, blue, white, green, blue, white, green. Predict the colors of the next 3 lights.

   _____

Name _____  Date _____

# Divide by 8

**Find each quotient.**

| Example  5 |
|---|
| 8)40 |

**1.** 8)16

**2.** 8)48

**3.** 8)8

**4.** 8)56

**5.** 8)24

**6.** 8)64

**7.** 8)32

**8.** 8)80

**9.** 8)72

**10.** $8 \div 8 =$

**11.** $64 \div 8 =$

**12.** $40 \div 8 =$

**13.** $24 \div 8 =$

**14.** $72 \div 8 =$

**15.** $56 \div 8 =$

**16.** $16 \div 8 =$

**17.** $80 \div 8 =$

**18.** $32 \div 8 =$

**19.** $48 \div 8 =$

## Problem Solving • Reasoning

**20.** Linda is washing windows. Each window has 8 panes. Linda washes 72 panes. How many windows does she wash?

**21.** There are 8 sponges in a box. If Linda buys 40 sponges, how many boxes does she buy?

**22.** Linda works for 40 hours. She works 8 hours a day. How many days does she work?

**23.** Linda washes windows in a house with 32 windows. There are 8 windows in each room. How many rooms are there?

Name _____     Date _____

# Divide by 9

**Find each quotient.**

| Example | 5 |
|---|---|
| | $9\overline{)45}$ |

**1.** $9\overline{)9}$

**2.** $9\overline{)72}$

**3.** $9\overline{)54}$

**4.** $9\overline{)18}$

**5.** $9\overline{)63}$

**6.** $9\overline{)27}$

**7.** $9\overline{)81}$

**8.** $9\overline{)36}$

**9.** $9\overline{)90}$

**10.** $18 \div 9$

**11.** $81 \div 9$

**12.** $9 \div 9$

**13.** $63 \div 9$

**14.** $27 \div 9$

_____  _____  _____  _____  _____

**15.** $90 \div 9$

**16.** $72 \div 9$

**17.** $36 \div 9$

**18.** $54 \div 9$

**19.** $45 \div 9$

_____  _____  _____  _____  _____

## Problem Solving • Reasoning

**20.** Chet builds 9 birdhouses every day. If Chet builds a total of 54 birdhouses, how many days will it take?

_____

**21.** Jean builds model cars. It takes her 9 hours to build one car. If she spends 45 hours a week building cars, how many cars does she make?

_____

**22.** Chet sells 72 birdhouses at a craft fair. He sells 9 birdhouses each day. How many days does he work at the fair?

_____

**23.** There are 9 tubes of paint in a box. Jean buys 63 tubes of paint. How many boxes does she buy?

_____

Name _____     Date _____

# Problem-Solving Application: Use Money

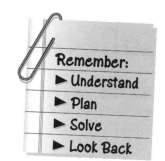

Remember:
► Understand
► Plan
► Solve
► Look Back

Addition, subtraction, multiplication, and division will help you solve a problem about money.

**Use the sign to solve each problem.**

**1.** Mrs. Bayne's class went to the zoo. Mrs. Bayne bought 3 toy animals. She bought 1 elephant and 2 tigers. How much did Mrs. Bayne spend?

**Think:** What was the price of the animals?

_____

**2.** Pat bought a book in the gift shop. If he pays with a $5 bill, what is his change?
**Think:** What is the price of the book?

_____

```
ZOO GIFT SHOP
TIGER          $2
LION           $3
ELEPHANT       $4
GUIDE BOOK     $4
POSTCARDS      20¢ EACH
```

**3.** Claudia bought 2 tigers and 1 book. She gave the clerk a $10 bill. What was her change?

_____

**4.** William had $10 to spend at the zoo gift shop. How many toy lions could he buy?

_____

**Use the sign to solve. Use these or other strategies.**

═══ **Problem-Solving Strategies** ═══

• Write a Number Sentence  • Use Logical Thinking   • Draw a Picture   • Guess and Check

**5.** Jack spent $10 at the gift shop. How many books and postcards could he buy?

_____

**6.** Forrest had $20. How many toy tigers could he buy?

_____

Name _____  Date _____

# Collecting and Organizing Data

**Use the tally chart to answer Questions 1–7.**

| Our Favorite Drink | | |
|---|---|---|
| **Drink** | **Tally** | **Total** |
| Juice | ⅢⅠ Ⅰ | 6 |
| Milk | ⅠⅠⅠⅠ | 4 |
| Soda | ⅠⅠⅠ | 3 |
| Water | ⅢⅠ | 5 |

**Example**

How many children chose milk as their favorite drink?

4 children

**1.** How many children chose soda as their favorite drink?

_____

**2.** How many children prefer either water or juice?

_____

**3.** How many more children prefer water than soda?

_____

**4.** Which is the least favorite drink?

_____

**5.** How many children prefer either milk or juice?

_____

**6.** How many more children prefer milk than soda?

_____

**7.** How many children voted?

_____

## Problem Solving • Reasoning

**8.** In Judy's class survey, 5 students chose apples as their favorite fruit. 2 more students preferred oranges than apples. How many students chose oranges as their favorite fruit?

_____

**9.** All 18 students in Kyle's class chose a number from 1 to 3. 7 students chose either 1 or 2. How many students chose number 3?

_____

Name _____     Date _____

# Use Line Plots

This line plot shows the number of goals scored by players in the soccer season.

**Soccer Goals Scored**

---

**Example**

How many players scored 4 goals?

None

---

**1.** How many players scored 3 goals?

_____

**2.** How many players scored no goals?

_____

**3.** What is the range of the data? What is the mode?

_____

**4.** How many players scored fewer than 2 goals?

_____

**5.** How many players scored at least 3 goals?

_____

**6.** How many players scored more than 5 goals?

_____

**7.** How many players scored 5 goals?

_____

## Problem Solving • Reasoning

**8.** Suppose another X was placed above the 4 on the line plot. Will the range and the mode of the data change?

_____

_____

**9.** Is it possible to tell the final scores of the games? Explain your reasoning.

_____

_____

_____

Name _____  Date _____

# Make a Pictograph

**Use the table to complete the pictograph.**

**Example**

**Favorite Sport**

Football    5
Basketball  9
Baseball    3
Soccer      12

| Favorite Sport | |
|---|---|
| Football | ○ ○ ◖ |
| Basketball | ○ ○ ○ ○ ◖ |
| Baseball | ○ ◖ |
| Soccer | ○ ○ ○ ○ ○ ○ |

Each ○ stands for 2 votes.

**1. Videos owned**

Mom     6
Dad     8
Tom     12
Tracey  14
Nathan  10

| Videos Owned | |
|---|---|
| Mom | |
| Dad | |
| Tom | |
| Tracey | |
| Nathan | |

Each 📼 stands for 4 videos.

**2. Museum Visitors**

Tuesday    56
Wednesday  48
Thursday   28
Friday     64

| Museum Visitors | |
|---|---|
| Tuesday | |
| Wednesday | |
| Thursday | |
| Friday | |

Each 🧍 stands for 8 people.

## Problem Solving • Reasoning

**3.** Suppose Nathan bought 4 more videos. How many 📼 would you need to draw next to Nathan?

_____

**4.** Suppose the key changed so that each 📼 stands for 2 videos. How many 📼 would you draw for Dad?

_____

Name _____ Date _____

# Problem-Solving Skill: Use a Bar Graph

Sometimes you can use the information from a bar graph to solve a problem.

**Use the graph for Problems 1–4.**

1. How many pages did Jason read on Tuesday?

   **Think:** At what number does the bar end?

   _____

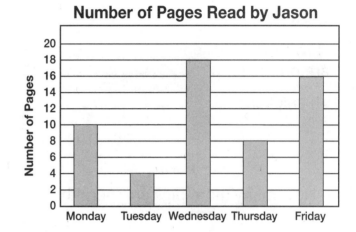

**Number of Pages Read by Jason**

2. How many more pages did Jason read on Wednesday than on Monday?

   **Think:** How much longer is the bar for Wednesday than for Monday?

   _____

3. How many more pages did Jason read on the day with the greatest number of pages than on the day with the least number of pages?

   _____

**Solve. Use these and other strategies.**

### Problem-Solving Strategies

- Write a Number Sentence • Draw a Picture • Use Models: Act It Out • Use Logical Thinking

4. Jason read twice as many pages of a different book on Saturday as he did on Monday. How many pages did he read on Saturday?

   _____

5. *Willow* has more pages than *Peace*. *Tales* has more pages than *Willow*. *Run* has the fewest pages. Write the titles in order from the longest to the shortest book.

   _____

Name _____     Date _____

# Make a Bar Graph

**Use the bar graph for Questions 1–8.**

| Example |
| --- |
| How many chickens are on the farm? |
| 10 chickens |

**Animals on the Farm**

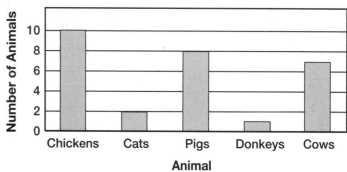

1. How many more pigs are there than cows?

   _____

2. How many cats and chickens are there on the farm?

   _____

3. How many animals are on the farm in all?

   _____

4. How many more chickens than cows are on the farm?

   _____

5. How many different types of animals live on the farm?

   _____

6. How many donkeys are on the farm?

   _____

## Problem Solving • Reasoning

7. Suppose dogs live on the farm. The bar for the number of dogs is longer than the bar for the number of pigs, but shorter than the bar for the number of chickens. How many dogs are there?

   _____

8. Suppose you want to make a bar graph to show the following number of animals on a farm: 40 pigs, 20 cows, 50 chickens, 10 cats. What would be a good scale for the graph?

   _____

Name _____ Date _____

# Graph Ordered Pairs

Write the ordered pair that describes where different things are found on the graph.

| Example |
|---|
| Bus Stop |
| (2, 5) |

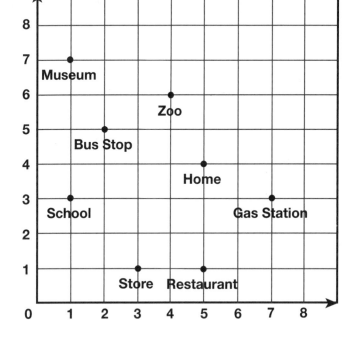

**1.** Store

_____

**2.** Restaurant

_____

**3.** Museum

_____

## What is located at the point for each ordered pair?

**4.** (1, 3)

_____

**5.** (7, 3)

_____

**6.** (5, 4)

_____

**7.** (4, 6)

_____

## Problem Solving • Reasoning

**8.** Draw a straight line between the school and the store. Write an ordered pair for another point on the line.

_____

**9.** Which is closer to home, the zoo or the museum?

_____

Name _____ Date _____

# Problem-Solving Strategy: Make a Table

Remember:
► Understand
► Plan
► Solve
► Look Back

You can make a table to help solve problems.

**Make a table to help you solve each problem.**

1. Every time Mark saves 3 pennies, Kathy saves 5 pennies. How many pennies will Kathy save when Mark saves 15 pennies?

   **Think:** What will be the headings on my table?

   _____

2. Julie is making 7 bracelets of different sizes. The smallest has 6 beads. Each bracelet needs to be 2 beads larger than the one before. How many beads will Julie need in all?

   **Think:** How many columns do I need in my table?

   _____

**Solve. Use these or other strategies.**

┌─────── **Problem-Solving Strategies** ───────┐
• Write a Number Sentence   • Make a Table   • Guess and Check   • Use Logical Reasoning

3. Jeremy has 5 bags of marbles. Each bag contains 10 marbles. He gives one bag to Mike and one bag to Susan. How many marbles does he have left?

   _____

4. A sloth is an animal that has 3 toes on each of its 4 feet. How many toes do 2 sloths have?

   _____

5. Greg sells tennis balls. Each can contains 3 balls. If he sells 12 tennis balls and has 18 left, how many cans did he begin with?

   _____

6. If you buy 3 muffins, the baker will give you one free muffin. If you buy 12 muffins, how many muffins do you get in all?

   _____

Name _____ Date _____

# Probability

**Write the word *certain*, *likely*, *unlikely*, or *impossible*
to describe the chance of picking a black marble.**

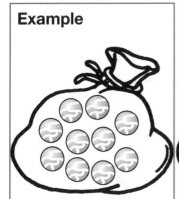

Example

impossible

1. _____

2. _____

3. _____

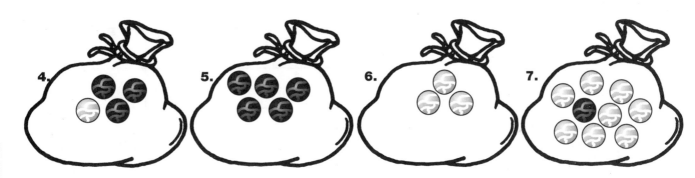

4. _____

5. _____

6. _____

7. _____

## Problem Solving • Reasoning

8. Draw a set of red and yellow circles from which it is likely to pick a yellow circle.

_____

9. Draw a set of circles from which it is certain to pick a red circle.

_____

Name _____  Date _____

# Recording Outcomes

**Complete the spinner experiment.**

**1.** Make a spinner like the one at the right.

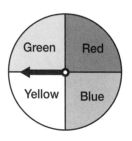

**2.** Spin the spinner 20 times. Record your results on the tally chart at the right.

| Spinner Experiment | | |
|---|---|---|
| **Outcome** | **Tally** | **Total** |
| Red | | |
| Blue | | |
| Yellow | | |
| Green | | |

**3.** Record your results on the line plot at the right.

## Problem Solving • Reasoning

**4.** How many Xs should you put on the line plot in all? What does this number represent?

_____

**5.** Is it likely, unlikely, certain, or impossible that the spinner in the experiment above will land on black?

_____

Name _____   Date _____

# Make Predictions

**Predict the outcome. Then test your prediction.**

**1.** Look at the spinner. Which color do you predict is likely to occur most often?

_____

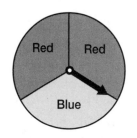

**2.** Make a spinner like the one shown. Spin the spinner 40 times. Record your results on the tally chart. Was your prediction correct?

| Spinner Experiment | | |
|---|---|---|
| **Outcome** | **Tally** | **Total** |
| Red | | |
| Blue | | |

## Problem Solving • Reasoning

**3.** Suppose you spin the spinner above one more time. Is it certain, impossible, likely, or unlikely that you will spin

red? _____

blue? _____

yellow? _____

red or blue? _____

**4.** There are 20 students in Mr. Choy's class. Two of the students are left-handed. Suppose Mr. Choy picked one student's name from a bag without looking. Is he more likely to choose a left-handed or a right-handed student?

_____

Name _____ Date _____

# Problem-Solving Application: Use Probability

Remember:
► Understand
► Plan
► Solve
► Look Back

Sometimes using what you know about probability can help you solve a problem.

Hilary and Andy are using the spinner at the right to play a game. Hilary moves forward 1 space when the spinner stops on an even number. Andy moves forward 1 space when the spinner stops on an odd number. Use what you know about probability to solve each problem.

**1.** Is the game fair?

**Think:** How many odd and even numbers are there?

_____

**2.** Who is more likely to win the game? Why?

**Think:** How many are there?

_____

**3.** How could Hilary and Andy use the spinner to make the game fair?

_____

**4.** Draw a spinner you could use to play a fair game.

**Solve. Use these or other strategies.**

### Problem-Solving Strategies

| • Use Logical Thinking | • Act It Out | • Write a Number Sentence | • Draw a Picture |

**5.** Diego begins at *Start.* He moves his game piece 3 squares forward, then 5 squares forward, and then lands on a square that says, "Go back 4 squares." How many squares from *Start* is Diego's game piece now?

_____

**6.** Tasha has cutout shapes. She has 3 more circles than squares. She has 4 fewer triangles than circles. She has 5 more stars than circles. If she has 3 triangles, how many of each of the other shapes does she have?

_____

Name _____ Date _____

# Fractions and Regions

**Write a fraction for the shaded part. Then write a fraction for the part that is not shaded.**

**Example**

Shaded: $\dfrac{3}{8}$

Not shaded: $\dfrac{5}{8}$

**1.**

Shaded: _____

Not shaded: _____

**2.**

Shaded: _____

Not shaded: _____

**3.**

Shaded: _____

Not shaded: _____

**4.**

Shaded: _____

Not shaded: _____

**5.**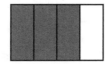

Shaded: _____

Not shaded: _____

**6.**

Shaded: _____

Not shaded: _____

**7.**

Shaded: _____

Not shaded: _____

## Problem Solving • Reasoning

**8.** Simon's comforter has five stripes of equal size. The colors of the stripes are red, yellow, red, yellow, red. Write a fraction for the red part of the comforter.

_____

**9.** Gabriel made a flag. It consists of 2 white stripes and 7 blue stripes. All the stripes are the same size. What fraction of the flag is white?

_____

Name _____ Date _____

# Fractions and Groups

**Write a fraction for each part of the group that is square.**

**Example**
⃝ ☐ △ ⃝ ⃝ △
⃝ ☐ △ ⃝

$\frac{2}{9}$

**1.**

_____

**2.**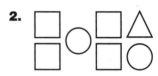

_____

**3.** ☐ ☐ ☐
☐ ☐ △

_____

**4.**

_____

**5.** ☐ ⃝ ☐ △

_____

**6.**

_____

**7.** ⃝ ⃝ ⃝ △
△ △ ☐ ⃝

_____

**8.**

_____

**9.** ☐ ⃝

_____

**10.** △ ☐ △ ☐ △

_____

**11.** ⃝ ☐ △

_____

## Problem Solving • Reasoning

**12.** Maria made a group of 5 stars and 3 diamonds. What part of the group is diamonds?

_____

**13.** Kirstie is making a pattern out of colored buttons. For every 4 blue buttons Kirstie uses, she uses 3 green buttons. She has used 21 buttons in her design. How many are blue?

_____

Name _____  Date _____

# Compare Fractions

Compare the fractions. Write > or < for each .

**Example**

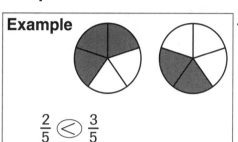

$\frac{2}{5}$ < $\frac{3}{5}$

**1.**

$\frac{8}{9}$ ◯ $\frac{2}{9}$

**2.**

$\frac{3}{3}$ ◯ $\frac{0}{3}$

**3.**

$\frac{2}{6}$ ◯ $\frac{5}{6}$

**4.**

$\frac{1}{4}$ ◯ $\frac{1}{6}$

**5.**

$\frac{5}{10}$ ◯ $\frac{9}{10}$

**6.**

$\frac{1}{8}$ ◯ $\frac{1}{3}$

**7.**

$\frac{1}{5}$ ◯ $\frac{0}{5}$

**8.**

$\frac{7}{9}$ ◯ $\frac{5}{9}$

**9.**

$\frac{1}{3}$ ◯ $\frac{3}{3}$

**10.**

$\frac{1}{4}$ ◯ $\frac{1}{9}$

**11.**

$\frac{1}{6}$ ◯ $\frac{1}{3}$

## Problem Solving • Reasoning

**12.** Donnie and Mark painted their skateboards. One fifth of Donnie's skateboard is yellow, and $\frac{1}{2}$ of Mark's is yellow. Whose has more yellow than any other color?

_____

**13.** Val has 20 CDs. She is putting them into boxes. Each box will fit 4 CDs. How many boxes does she need?

_____

Name _____ Date _____

# Order Fractions

**Order the fractions from least to greatest.**

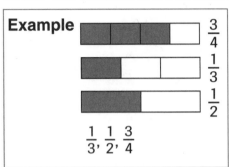

Example $\frac{3}{4}$ $\frac{1}{3}$ $\frac{1}{2}$

$\frac{1}{3}, \frac{1}{2}, \frac{3}{4}$

1. 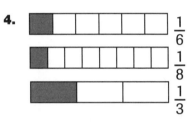 $\frac{2}{3}$ $\frac{1}{3}$ $\frac{1}{4}$

_____

2. 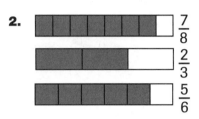 $\frac{7}{8}$ $\frac{2}{3}$ $\frac{5}{6}$

_____

3. 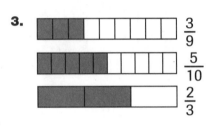 $\frac{3}{9}$ $\frac{5}{10}$ $\frac{2}{3}$

_____

4. 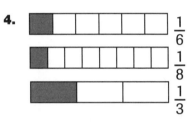 $\frac{1}{6}$ $\frac{1}{8}$ $\frac{1}{3}$

_____

5. 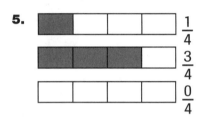 $\frac{1}{4}$ $\frac{3}{4}$ $\frac{0}{4}$

_____

6. 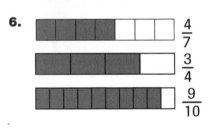 $\frac{4}{7}$ $\frac{3}{4}$ $\frac{9}{10}$

_____

7. 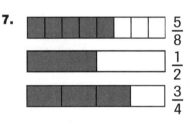 $\frac{5}{8}$ $\frac{1}{2}$ $\frac{3}{4}$

_____

8. 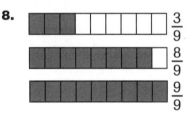 $\frac{3}{9}$ $\frac{8}{9}$ $\frac{9}{9}$

_____

## Problem Solving • Reasoning

9. At the local store, nuts cost $0.78 for $\frac{1}{4}$ pound. Sean wants to buy $\frac{3}{4}$ pound of nuts. How much will this cost him?

_____

10. Sean wants to share his bag of nuts with Tony. He gives Tony $\frac{2}{3}$ of the nuts and has the rest himself. Who has more nuts, Sean or Tony?

_____

Name _____ Date _____

# Modeling Equivalent Fractions

**Write *equivalent* or *not equivalent*.**

**Example**

**equivalent**

**1.**

_____

**2.**

_____

**3.**

_____

**Name the equivalent fractions.**

**4.**

_____

**5.**

_____

## Problem Solving • Reasoning

**6.** Brian and Martin both order similar pizzas. Brian cuts his pizza into three equal pieces and eats two of the pieces. Martin cuts his pizza into six equal pieces and eats four of the pieces. Have they eaten the same amount of pizza? Explain.

_____

**7.** Grant drew a square and divided it into 9 equal parts. He shaded 6 of the parts. Nate drew a square the same size and divided his square into 3 equal parts. How many parts should Nate shade so that he has the same amount shaded as Grant?

_____

Name _____     Date _____

# Find Equivalent Fractions

**Write *equivalent* or *not equivalent*. Draw fraction strips to support your answer.**

| **Example** $\frac{1}{4}$ and $\frac{2}{8}$ |
|---|
| $\frac{1}{4}$ and $\frac{2}{8}$ are equivalent. |

**1.** $\frac{4}{5}$ and $\frac{5}{8}$

_____

**2.** $\frac{2}{3}$ and $\frac{6}{9}$

_____

| 1 whole | | | |
|---|---|---|---|
| $\frac{1}{4}$ | | | |
| $\frac{1}{8}$ $\frac{1}{8}$ | | | | | |

**3.** $\frac{1}{2}$ and $\frac{4}{8}$

_____

**4.** $\frac{3}{4}$ and $\frac{7}{8}$

_____

**5.** $\frac{3}{5}$ and $\frac{4}{6}$

_____

**6.** $\frac{3}{3}$ and $\frac{7}{7}$

_____

**7.** $\frac{2}{4}$ and $\frac{5}{10}$

_____

**8.** $\frac{1}{5}$ and $\frac{3}{10}$

_____

## Problem Solving • Reasoning

**9.** A pizza is cut into 12 equal pieces. How many pieces will Mary get if she has $\frac{1}{4}$ of the pizza?

_____

**10.** Jodie is thinking of a fraction that is equivalent to $\frac{1}{3}$. The numerator of Jodie's fraction is 3. What is the denominator?

_____

Name _____  Date _____

# Problem-Solving Strategy: Choose a Strategy

Remember:
► Understand
► Plan
► Solve
► Look Back

**Before starting to solve a problem, you should decide which strategy to use.**

**Choose a strategy to solve each problem.**

1. Mrs. Taylor has 6 books. She gives one book to each of 4 students. What fraction of the books does she give away?

   **Think:** How could I draw a picture to solve the problem?

   _____

2. Three fifths of Greg's class are girls. Four tenths of the class are boys. Are there more boys or girls in the class?

   **Think:** Do I need to know the total number of children in the class?

   _____

3. A school banner has 8 equal parts. One half of the panels are green and one fourth of the panels are blue. The rest of the banner is yellow. How many panels are yellow?

   _____

4. Troy has a collection of books. One half of the books are about animals, $\frac{1}{8}$ of the books are about sports, and $\frac{1}{3}$ of the books are about trains. What kind of book does he have the most of?

   _____

**Solve. Use these or other strategies.**

| Problem-Solving Strategies |
|---|
| • Find a Pattern • Guess and Check • Draw a Picture • Use Logical Thinking |

5. Toby and Carl have an equal number of marbles. Five eights of Toby's marbles are white, and $\frac{5}{6}$ of Carl's marbles are white. Who has more white marbles?

   _____

6. Jordan is making a collage out of 20 coins. He places the coins in order: penny, nickel, penny, dime, penny, nickel, penny, dime. If he continues this pattern, how many pennies will he use?

   _____

Name _____ Date _____

# Fractional Parts of a Group

**Use counters to find each answer.**

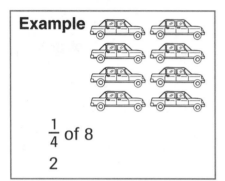

**Example**

$\frac{1}{4}$ of 8

2

**1.** $\frac{1}{3}$ of 12

_____

**2.** $\frac{1}{7}$ of 7

_____

**Draw a picture to find each answer.**

**3.** $\frac{1}{2}$ of 8

_____

**4.** $\frac{1}{3}$ of 15

_____

**5.** $\frac{1}{5}$ of 10

_____

**6.** $\frac{1}{12}$ of 12

_____

**7.** $\frac{1}{4}$ of 16

_____

**8.** $\frac{1}{3}$ of 9

_____

**9.** $\frac{1}{8}$ of 8

_____

**10.** $\frac{1}{2}$ of 14

_____

**11.** $\frac{1}{3}$ of 18

_____

**12.** $\frac{1}{9}$ of 18

_____

**13.** $\frac{1}{4}$ of 12

_____

**14.** $\frac{1}{5}$ of 20

_____

**15.** $\frac{1}{6}$ of 18

_____

**16.** $\frac{1}{2}$ of 2

_____

**17.** $\frac{1}{8}$ of 24

_____

**18.** $\frac{1}{2}$ of 12

_____

## Problem Solving • Reasoning

**19.** Curtis has 18 sandwiches. One sixth are tuna. How many tuna sandwiches does Curtis have?

_____

**20.** Mrs. Dixon buys one dozen bagels. One fourth are blueberry bagels. How many blueberry bagels does Mrs. Dixon buy?

_____

Name _____  Date _____

# Mixed Numbers

Write an improper fraction and a mixed number for each.

**Example**

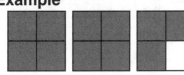

$\frac{11}{4}$, $2\frac{3}{4}$

**1.**

_____

**2.**

_____

**3.**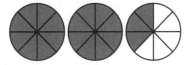

_____

**4.**

_____

**5.**

_____

Write each as a whole or a mixed number.

**6.** $\frac{12}{5}$

_____

**7.** $\frac{3}{2}$

_____

**8.** $\frac{17}{3}$

_____

**9.** $\frac{18}{6}$

_____

**10.** $\frac{13}{4}$

_____

**11.** $\frac{11}{3}$

_____

**12.** $\frac{7}{6}$

_____

**13.** $\frac{12}{2}$

_____

## Problem Solving • Reasoning

**14.** John uses six $\frac{1}{3}$-cups of flour in his muffin recipe. Mindy uses 2 cups. Who uses more flour?

_____

**15.** A recipe says that you need $\frac{6}{4}$ tablespoons of flour. Brady has 1 tablespoon of flour left. Does he have enough for the recipe?

_____

Name _____     Date _____

# Add and Subtract Fractions

**Use the pictures to help you add or subtract.**

**Example**

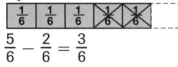

$$\frac{5}{6} - \frac{2}{6} = \frac{3}{6}$$

**1.**

$$\frac{1}{10} + \frac{6}{10} =$$

_____

**2.**

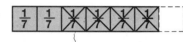

$$\frac{6}{7} - \frac{4}{7} =$$

_____

**3.**

$$\frac{5}{9} - \frac{1}{9} =$$

_____

**4.**

$$\frac{1}{3} + \frac{2}{3} =$$

_____

**5.**

$$\frac{4}{4} - \frac{3}{4} =$$

_____

**Add or subtract. Use fraction strips or draw a picture to help you.**

**6.** $\frac{5}{7} + \frac{1}{7}$

_____

**7.** $\frac{3}{8} - \frac{1}{8}$

_____

**8.** $\frac{9}{10} - \frac{4}{10}$

_____

**9.** $\frac{1}{6} + \frac{1}{6}$

_____

**10.** $\frac{3}{8} - \frac{2}{8}$

_____

**11.** $\frac{6}{9} - \frac{4}{9}$

_____

**12.** $\frac{4}{8} + \frac{2}{8}$

_____

**13.** $\frac{5}{5} - \frac{2}{5}$

_____

## Problem Solving • Reasoning

**14.** Ruth and Sara shared a bag of pretzels. Ruth ate $\frac{1}{4}$ of the bag and Sara ate $\frac{2}{4}$ of the bag. How much did they eat in all?

_____

**15.** Richard made a sub sandwich that used 12 ounces of meat. He used 5 ounces of beef and 3 ounces of turkey. Write a number sentence to find out what fraction of the total ounces of meat were beef and turkey.

_____

Name _____  Date _____

# Problem-Solving Skill: Multistep Problems

Sometimes it takes more than one step to solve a problem.

**Solve.**

1. There are 24 bottles of juice in Sam's refrigerator. One half of the bottles are apple juice. He gives $\frac{1}{4}$ of the bottles of apple juice to his friends. How many bottles of apple juice does he give away?

   **Think:** What do I need to find out first?

   _____

2. Pete delivers 10 pizzas in the afternoon and 10 pizzas in the evening. One fifth of the pizzas are Super Duper Specials. How many Super Duper Specials does he deliver?

   **Think:** How many steps do you need to do?

   _____

3. Kate has 10 apples and 3 oranges. She puts $\frac{1}{2}$ of the apples and $\frac{1}{3}$ of the oranges in a fruit basket. How many pieces of fruit does she have left?

   _____

4. Raoul has 4 apple muffins and 6 lemon muffins. He gives $\frac{1}{5}$ of the muffins to his friends. How many muffins does he have left?

   _____

**Solve. Use these or other strategies to solve each problem.**

| Problem-Solving Strategies |
|---|
| • Act It Out    • Find a Pattern    • Draw a Picture |

5. Members of a band line up in 5 rows of 10 people. One half of the band members play woodwind instruments. How many people play woodwind instruments?

   _____

6. Jude paints his kite with these stripes: red, green, blue, blue, red, green, blue, blue, red. What are the colors of the next 3 stripes likely to be?

   _____

Name _____   Date _____

# Tenths

**Write a fraction and a decimal for each shaded part.**

| **Example** | **1.**  | **2.**  |
|---|---|---|
| 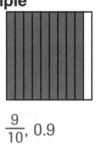 $\frac{9}{10}$, 0.9 | _____ | _____ |

| **3.**  | **4.**  | **5.** 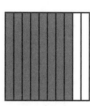 |
|---|---|---|
| _____ | _____ | _____ |

**Write each as a decimal.**

**6.** $\frac{2}{10}$          **7.** $\frac{7}{10}$          **8.** $\frac{5}{10}$          **9.** $\frac{2}{10}$

_____      _____      _____      _____

**10.** nine tenths    **11.** six tenths    **12.** seven tenths    **13.** three tenths

_____      _____      _____      _____

## Problem Solving • Reasoning

**14.** Simon used three tenths of a bag of flour to make a cake. Write a decimal for the amount of flour Simon used.

_____

**15.** A bag contains 10 apples. Seven tenths of the apples are red. What decimal represents the portion of the apples that are not red?

_____

Name _____     Date _____

# Hundredths

**Write a fraction and a decimal for each shaded part.**

**Example**

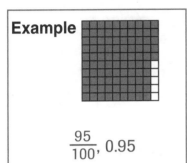

$\frac{95}{100}$, 0.95

**1.**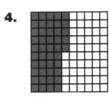

_____

**2.**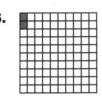

_____

**3.**

_____

**4.**

_____

**5.**

_____

**Write each as a decimal.**

**6.** $\frac{23}{100}$

_____

**7.** $\frac{85}{100}$

_____

**8.** $\frac{5}{100}$

_____

**9.** $\frac{64}{100}$

_____

**10.** nine hundredths

_____

**11.** sixty-two hundredths

_____

**12.** seventy hundredths

_____

## Problem Solving • Reasoning

**13.** Ben's book has 100 pages. Ben has read 38 pages. Write a decimal that shows that part of the book Ben has already read.

_____

**14.** Malcolm has read 0.82 of his magazine. How much of the magazine has he *not* read?

_____

Name _____  Date _____

# Decimals Greater Than 1

**Write a mixed number and a decimal for the shaded part.**

**Example**

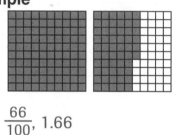

$\frac{66}{100}$, 1.66

**1.**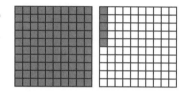

_____

**2.**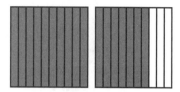

_____

**3.**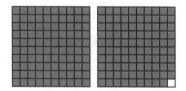

_____

**4.**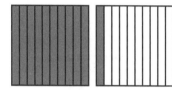

_____

**5.**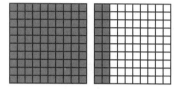

_____

**Write each as a decimal.**

**6.** $5\frac{3}{10}$

_____

**7.** $2\frac{34}{100}$

_____

**8.** $8\frac{9}{10}$

_____

**9.** $6\frac{21}{100}$

_____

**10.** nine and thirty-five hundredths

_____

**11.** one and seventy-six hundredths

_____

## Problem Solving • Reasoning

**12.** Jessica's height is $1\frac{1}{10}$ meters. Write a decimal that shows Jessica's height.

_____

**13.** A box of matches contains 100 matches. For his camping trip, Hugh packs 2 whole boxes and $\frac{25}{100}$ of a box. Write a decimal for the number of boxes of matches that Hugh is taking.

_____

Name _____ Date _____

# Compare and Order Fractions and Decimals

**Compare. Write >, <, or = for each ◯.**

| Example |
|---|
| 1.3 > 1.28 |

**1.** 6.3 ◯ 7.03

**2.** 0.45 ◯ 0.5

**3.** 3.20 ◯ 3.2

**4.** 0.53 ◯ 0.20

**5.** 4.06 ◯ 4.10

**6.** 1.3 ◯ 1.8

**7.** $9\frac{9}{10}$ ◯ 9.10

**8.** 8.2 ◯ 8.20

**9.** $\frac{13}{100}$ ◯ 0.19

**10.** 6.2 ◯ 6.19

**11.** 2.21 ◯ 2.39

**12.** 3.3 ◯ 3.87

**13.** $1\frac{3}{100}$ ◯ 1.01

**14.** 1.00 ◯ 1.0

**15.** 7.18 ◯ 7.2

**Order from least to greatest.**

**16.** 3.6  3.50,  4.03

_____

**17.** 0.5  $\frac{30}{100}$  0.27

_____

**18.** 7.77  6.87  8.67

_____

**19.** $2\frac{4}{100}$  2.40  2.24

_____

**20.** 1.50  0.99  1.9

_____

**21.** 0.10  0.05  0.01

_____

## Problem Solving • Reasoning

**22.** The record for running 50 yards is 12.4 seconds. Clive ran 50 yards in 12.3 seconds. Did he break the record?

_____

**23.** The minimum height for a ride at a theme park is 1.20 meters. Josh measures 1.4 meters. Can he go on the ride?

_____

Name _____     Date _____

# Add and Subtract Decimals

**Add or subtract.**

| Example | 5.2 |
|---|---|
| | + 3.4 |
| | 8.6 |

**1.**    6.8
      + 1.9

**2.**    8.98
      − 5.56

**3.**    5.79
      + 4.11

**4.**    2.6
      − 1.8

**5.**    4.01
      − 3.40

**6.**    7.94
      + 1.43

**7.**    2.04
      + 3.40

**8.** 4.30 + 3.81

**9.** 3.03 − 0.80

**10.** 0.82 − 0.79

**11.** 0.99 + 0.88

_____

_____

_____

_____

**12.** 3.17 − 2.55

**13.** 4.81 + 0.19

**14.** 3.25 − 0.79

**15.** 6.1 − 4.3

_____

_____

_____

_____

## Problem Solving • Reasoning

**16.** Susan's tower is 2.30 meters high. Ralph's tower is 1.86 meters high. Whose tower is higher? How much higher?

_____

**17.** James has 2 building blocks. One is 0.46 meters high and the other is 0.72 meters high. What is the total height of the blocks if James puts one on top of the other?

_____

Name _____  Date _____

# Decimals, Fractions, and Money

**Write the fractional part of $1. Then write the amount using a dollar sign and decimal point.**

**Example** 50 pennies

Fractional Part of $1:

$\frac{50}{100}$ or $\frac{1}{2}$; $0.50

**1.** 3 dimes

Fractional Part of $1:

_____

**2.** 3 quarters

Fractional Part of $1:

_____

**3.** 1 half-dollar
Fractional Part of $1:

_____

**4.** 6 dimes
Fractional Part of $1:

_____

**5.** 30 pennies
Fractional Part of $1:

_____

**6.** 9 dimes
Fractional Part of $1:

_____

**7.** 5 pennies
Fractional Part of $1:

_____

**8.** 10 dimes
Fractional Part of $1:

_____

## Problem Solving • Reasoning

**9.** Cliff paid for his milk with 3 quarters. He received no change. What was the price of the milk?

_____

**10.** At Ms. Cromer's bakery, bread rolls cost $\frac{4}{10}$ of a dollar. How many dimes would Tina need to buy a bread roll?

_____

Name _____ Date _____

# Problem-Solving Application: Use Money

**Solve.**

1. Steve bought a bottle of water for $0.80 and a sandwich for $2.10. Steve paid with three $1 bills. His change was given in nickels. How many nickels did he receive?

   **Think:** What was the value of his change?

   _____

2. Donna's check at a restaurant came to $7.32. She paid with seven $1 bills and 2 quarters. What was her change?

   **Think:** How much money did she give?

   _____

3. Fiona ordered a bowl of chili for $3.99 and a glass of milk for $1.25. She paid with one $5 bill, 2 quarters, and 8 dimes. What was her change?

   _____

4. Mary bought a pencil for $1.35 and a ruler for $1.10. How much more did the pencil cost?

   _____

**Solve. Use these and other strategies.**

╭─────────────── Problem-Solving Strategies ───────────────╮

• Use Logical Thinking        • Act It Out        • Write a Number Sentence

╰──────────────────────────────────────────────────────────╯

5. Sheila wants to buy as many bags of pretzels as possible. Pretzels cost $1.60 for each bag. Sheila has $5.00. How many bags can she buy?

   _____

6. Robin spent $5.00 on 2 cards and one sheet of wrapping paper. The cards cost $1.90 each. How much did the wrapping paper cost?

   _____

7. Daryl has 5 quarters and 4 dimes. Can he buy a notebook that costs $1.50?

   _____

8. Julie has $1.00. She gives 40 cents to Chris, and than half of the remainder of the money to Chloe. How much does she have left?

   _____

Name _____ Date _____

# Mental Math: Multiply Multiples of 10, 100, and 1,000

| **Example** | $2 \times 7 = 14$ |
|---|---|
| | $2 \times 70 = 140$ |
| | $2 \times 700 = 1,400$ |
| | $2 \times 7,000 = 14,000$ |

**Find each product.**

**1.** $6 \times 7 =$ _____

$6 \times 70 =$ _____

$6 \times 700 =$ _____

$6 \times 7,000 =$ _____

**2.** $8 \times 9 =$ _____

$8 \times 90 =$ _____

$8 \times 900 =$ _____

$8 \times 9,000 =$ _____

**3.** $7 \times 80$

_____

**4.** $9 \times 6,000$

_____

**5.** $8 \times 200$

_____

**6.** $3 \times 80$

_____

**7.** $4 \times 7,000$

_____

**8.** $6 \times 2,000$

_____

**9.** $9 \times 400$

_____

**10.** $4 \times 40$

_____

**11.** $2 \times 900$

_____

**12.** $5 \times 90$

_____

**13.** $4 \times 8 =$ _____

$4 \times 80 =$ _____

$4 \times 800 =$ _____

$4 \times 8,000 =$ _____

**14.** $6 \times 4 =$ _____

$6 \times 40 =$ _____

$6 \times 400 =$ _____

$6 \times 4,000 =$ _____

**15.** $5 \times 9 =$ _____

$5 \times 90 =$ _____

$5 \times 900 =$ _____

$5 \times 9,000 =$ _____

## Problem Solving • Reasoning

**16.** Janet's mom is making a relish tray for the school party. She bought 9 different items to put on the tray. She wants 40 of each item on the tray. How many items in all will she have on the tray?

_____

**17.** James is taking nut trays to the party. Each tray has 200 almonds, 300 peanuts, and 100 pecans on it. How many nuts does he need if he makes 4 trays?

_____

Name _____     Date _____

# Modeling Multiplication

| Example |
| --- |
| $4 \times 13 = 52$ 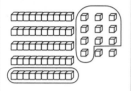 |

**Use base-ten blocks to help you multiply.**

**1.** $2 \times 15$              **2.** $5 \times 13$

_____             _____

**3.** $11 \times 4$              **4.** $16 \times 3$

_____             _____

**5.** $28 \times 5$    **6.** $22 \times 4$    **7.** $15 \times 6$    **8.** $38 \times 5$

_____     _____     _____     _____

**9.** $31 \times 9$    **10.** $23 \times 4$    **11.** $41 \times 7$    **12.** $16 \times 5$

_____     _____     _____     _____

**13.** $57 \times 6$    **14.** $35 \times 3$    **15.** $12 \times 9$    **16.** $46 \times 4$

_____     _____     _____     _____

**17.** $23 \times 3$    **18.** $41 \times 4$    **19.** $74 \times 2$    **20.** $13 \times 4$

_____     _____     _____     _____

**21.** $36 \times 4$    **22.** $85 \times 3$    **23.** $61 \times 6$    **24.** $42 \times 3$

_____     _____     _____     _____

**25.** $62 \times 7$    **26.** $94 \times 5$    **27.** $39 \times 6$    **28.** $18 \times 9$

_____     _____     _____     _____

Name _____ Date _____

# Two-Digit Numbers

**Example**

$3 \times 14 = \blacksquare$

$$\begin{array}{r} 14 \\ \times\ 3 \\ \hline 42 \end{array}$$

**Find each product.**

1. $4 \times 17 =$ _____

2. $5 \times 11 =$ _____

3. $\begin{array}{r} 36 \\ \times\ 2 \\ \hline \end{array}$
4. $\begin{array}{r} 22 \\ \times\ 6 \\ \hline \end{array}$
5. $\begin{array}{r} 27 \\ \times\ 3 \\ \hline \end{array}$
6. $\begin{array}{r} 43 \\ \times\ 5 \\ \hline \end{array}$
7. $\begin{array}{r} 34 \\ \times\ 4 \\ \hline \end{array}$

8. $\begin{array}{r} 29 \\ \times\ 4 \\ \hline \end{array}$
9. $\begin{array}{r} 38 \\ \times\ 8 \\ \hline \end{array}$
10. $\begin{array}{r} 19 \\ \times\ 6 \\ \hline \end{array}$
11. $\begin{array}{r} 46 \\ \times\ 9 \\ \hline \end{array}$
12. $\begin{array}{r} 26 \\ \times\ 6 \\ \hline \end{array}$

13. $\begin{array}{r} 87 \\ \times\ 5 \\ \hline \end{array}$
14. $\begin{array}{r} 37 \\ \times\ 9 \\ \hline \end{array}$
15. $\begin{array}{r} 45 \\ \times\ 6 \\ \hline \end{array}$
16. $\begin{array}{r} 39 \\ \times\ 9 \\ \hline \end{array}$
17. $\begin{array}{r} 67 \\ \times\ 7 \\ \hline \end{array}$

18. $\begin{array}{r} 68 \\ \times\ 3 \\ \hline \end{array}$
19. $\begin{array}{r} 79 \\ \times\ 9 \\ \hline \end{array}$
20. $\begin{array}{r} 88 \\ \times\ 8 \\ \hline \end{array}$
21. $\begin{array}{r} 73 \\ \times\ 6 \\ \hline \end{array}$
22. $\begin{array}{r} 67 \\ \times\ 9 \\ \hline \end{array}$

## Problem Solving • Reasoning

23. Susan was in charge of bringing the water for the soccer team. There are 16 girls on the team. If each girl needs 3 bottles of water, how many bottles does Susan need for the team?

24. Sam helped his dad plant sweet corn on their farm. They planted 9 rows with 45 corn plants in each row. How many plants did they plant in all?

Name _____  Date _____

# Three-Digit Numbers

| Example |
|---|
| $\overset{3}{116}$ <br> $\times\ 5$ <br> ___ <br> $580$ |

**Multiply.**

1. $419$
   $\times\ 2$

2. $119$
   $\times\ 5$

3. $217$
   $\times\ 4$

4. $325$
   $\times\ 3$

5. $232$
   $\times\ 4$

6. $121$
   $\times\ 7$

7. $317$
   $\times\ 3$

8. $246$
   $\times\ 2$

9. $115$
   $\times\ 6$

10. $146$
    $\times\ 2$

11. $162$
    $\times\ 4$

12. $311$
    $\times\ 3$

13. $419$
    $\times\ 2$

14. $225$
    $\times\ 3$

15. $2 \times 234$

16. $2 \times 393$

17. $4 \times 131$

18. $5 \times 116$

19. $7 \times 112$

20. $3 \times 142$

21. $3 \times 242$

22. $8 \times 112$

## Problem Solving • Reasoning

23. The third grade class donated toys to a children's hospital. They donated 3 toys for each child. If there were 119 children, how many toys did they donate in all?

24. Jamie's art class is making pictures out of tissue paper. Each student needs 115 small pieces of tissue paper. There are 8 students in the class. How many pieces of tissue paper are needed?

Name _____  Date _____

# Regrouping Twice

| Example |
|---|
| 31 |
| 152 |
| × 6 |
| ——— |
| 912 |

**Multiply.**

**1.** 619
× 3

**2.** 1,316
× 5

**3.** 194
× 5

**4.** 429
× 3

**5.** 149
× 7

**6.** 715
× 4

**7.** 828
× 2

**8.** 163
× 5

**9.** 1,191
× 6

**10.** 2,268
× 3

**11.** 414
× 7

**12.** 632
× 4

**13.** 375
× 2

**14.** 219
× 9

**15.** 521
× 8

**16.** 361
× 4

**17.** 712
× 6

**18.** 4,916
× 2

**19.** 149
× 3

## Problem Solving • Reasoning

**20.** Kristen is going for a vacation to California. It is 3,176 miles from her home. How many miles will Kristen travel to California and back?

**21.** John was in a book reading contest with 3 other contestants. All four of the readers had to read the same book, which was 1,972 pages. How many pages is this in all?

Name _____  Date _____

# Multiply Money

| Example |
|---|
| 1 3 |
| $2.29 |
| × 4 |
| —— |
| $9.16 |

**Multiply.**

**1.** $3.76
  × 2

**2.** $1.38
  × 3

**3.** $4.25
  × 4

**4.** $1.57
  × 5

**5.** $1.29
  × 3

**6.** $4.92
  × 2

**7.** $2.68
  × 8

**8.** $3.19
  × 3

**9.** $1.88
  × 4

**10.** $4.38
  × 2

**11.** $2.75
  × 3

**12.** $1.49
  × 4

**13.** $1.95
  × 5

**14.** $3.54
  × 2

**15.** $2.47
  × 3

**16.** $3.15
  × 5

**17.** $1.72
  × 2

**18.** $4.29
  × 4

**19.** $1.99
  × 3

## Problem Solving • Reasoning

**20.** Grapes were on sale at the store for $1.67 per pound. Nancy wanted to get three pounds of grapes. How much would that cost her?

_____

**21.** Sheila bought four slices of pizza. The pizza cost $1.99 per slice. How much did Sheila spend?

_____

Name _____ Date _____

# Problem-Solving Strategy: Solve a Simpler Problem

Remember:
► Understand
► Plan
► Solve
► Look Back

Sometimes a problem can be solved by first thinking about a simpler problem that has easier numbers.

**Solve.**

1. Diane's family is going on vacation. They intend on driving 455 miles the first day and 432 miles the second day. How many total miles will they have driven at the end of the second day?

   **Think:** What numbers could I use to make this problem simpler?

   _____

2. While on vacation, the Smith family walked 2 miles on the beach looking for shells. If one mile is equal to 1,760 yards, how many yards did they walk?

   **Think:** What numbers could I use to make this problem simpler?

   _____

3. Julie decided to go on a bike outing. She got tired after riding 880 yards. If a yard is equal to 3 feet, how many feet did Julie ride her bike?

   _____

4. Julie's brother rode his bike 960 yards before he got tired. She told him that she had ridden her bike for 880 yards. How much farther did Julie's brother ride?

   _____

**Solve. Use these or other strategies.**

┌─────────────────────── Problem-Solving Strategies ───────────────────────┐
• Write a Number Sentence • Guess and Check • Solve a Simpler Problem • Draw a Picture
└───────────────────────────────────────────────────────────────────────────┘

5. The girls roped off a rectangular area to set up their tents. The area was 46 feet long and 21 feet wide. How much rope did they use?

   _____

6. Cindy was selling sweet corn from her garden for $2.50 a dozen. She sold 9 dozen the first day. How much money did she make?

   _____

Name _____ Date _____

# Modeling Division With Remainders

Example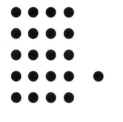

21 ÷ 5 = 4 R 1

**Write a division sentence for each model.**

1.

_____

2. ● ● ● ●
● ● ● ●
● ● ● ●  ● ●
● ● ● ●

_____

3. ● ● ● ● ● ●  ● ●
● ● ● ● ● ●

_____

**Divide.**

**4.** 12 ÷ 6

_____

**5.** 18 ÷ 3

_____

**6.** 23 ÷ 3

_____

**7.** 21 ÷ 4

_____

**8.** 36 ÷ 4

_____

**9.** 35 ÷ 4

_____

**10.** 26 ÷ 8

_____

**11.** 15 ÷ 5

_____

**12.** 15 ÷ 2

_____

**13.** 39 ÷ 8

_____

**14.** 19 ÷ 3

_____

**15.** 37 ÷ 9

_____

**16.** 48 ÷ 7

_____

**17.** 36 ÷ 5

_____

**18.** 64 ÷ 8

_____

**19.** 62 ÷ 8

_____

**20.** 33 ÷ 6

_____

**21.** 42 ÷ 7

_____

**22.** 41 ÷ 8

_____

**23.** 41 ÷ 6

_____

Name _____ Date _____

# Two-Digit Quotients

| Example |
|---|
| 11 R2 |
| 4$\overline{)46}$ |
| $-\ 4\!\downarrow$ |
| 06 |
| $-\ 4$ |
| 2 |

**Divide and check. Use base-ten blocks if you wish.**

1. 5$\overline{)59}$     2. 4$\overline{)82}$     3. 4$\overline{)48}$     4. 2$\overline{)49}$

5. 4$\overline{)48}$     6. 5$\overline{)52}$     7. 3$\overline{)69}$     8. 2$\overline{)42}$     9. 3$\overline{)37}$

10. 2$\overline{)83}$     11. 4$\overline{)84}$     12. 3$\overline{)94}$     13. 3$\overline{)97}$     14. 2$\overline{)26}$

15. 3$\overline{)92}$     16. 4$\overline{)57}$     17. 6$\overline{)77}$     18. 7$\overline{)84}$     19. 5$\overline{)56}$

## Problem Solving • Reasoning

20. Shaun picked 28 wildflowers. He wanted to divide them evenly between his mother and grandmother. How many flowers would each receive?

21. Marie had 84 streamers to hang for her party. She asked her three sisters to help her. She divided the streamers evenly. How many streamers did each girl hang?

_____     _____

Name _____ Date _____

# Problem-Solving Skill: Interpret Remainders

Sometimes you need to decide what to do with the remainder so that the answer is reasonable.

**1.** Mrs. Black gave each of her students 4 stickers to take home. If she started out with 97 stickers, how many students can get a complete set?

**Think:** Can a set be made with less than 4 stickers?

_____

**2.** Michele and 3 friends want to jump on her trampoline after school. They have only 30 minutes to play and they all want equal time on the trampoline. If they all jump exactly the same number of minutes and stay on the trampoline as long as they each can, how many minutes would not be used?

**Think:** Do you need to know how many minutes will be used or how many will not be used?

_____

**Solve. Use these or other strategies.**

┌─────────── **Problem-Solving Strategies** ───────────┐
• Use Logical Thinking   • Act It Out   • Write a Number Sentence   • Draw a Picture
└──────────────────────────────────────────────────┘

**3.** Cindy has 3 more games to play at her party. Her friends are supposed to go home in 50 minutes. If they spend the same amount of time on each game and spend the most time possible playing, how many minutes won't be used playing a game?

_____

**4.** Joanne made gift bags to hand out at her party. She put 5 items in each bag. She started out with 133 items. How many friends are coming to her party?

_____

Name _____ Date _____

# Regrouping in Division

| Example |
|---|
| 13 R2 |
| 5)67 |
| − 5 |
| 17 |
| −15 |
| 2 |

**Divide and check.**

**1.** 3)72     **2.** 4)72     **3.** 3)41     **4.** 2)39

**5.** 4)92     **6.** 5)72     **7.** 2)56     **8.** 3)55     **9.** 4)64

**10.** 5)98     **11.** 4)52     **12.** 3)64     **13.** 2)75     **14.** 5)85

**15.** 4)67     **16.** 3)49     **17.** 5)56     **18.** 6)77     **19.** 3)41

## Problem Solving • Reasoning

**20.** The marching band lined up for the half-time performance. They were split into 5 equal groups. There were 95 members in the band. How many band members were in each group?

**21.** The art teacher had 54 pieces of chalk to pass out to her students. If she divided the class into 3 groups, how many pieces of chalk would each group have?

_____     _____

Name _____    Date _____

# Three-Digit Quotients

| Example |
|---|
| $\begin{array}{r} 137 \\ 2\overline{)274} \\ -2 \\ \hline 07 \\ -6 \\ \hline 14 \\ -14 \\ \hline 0 \end{array}$ |

**Divide and check.**

**1.** $4\overline{)852}$    **2.** $3\overline{)948}$    **3.** $5\overline{)575}$    **4.** $4\overline{)464}$

**6.** $3\overline{)681}$    **7.** $2\overline{)496}$    **8.** $5\overline{)560}$    **9.** $3\overline{)375}$    **10.** $2\overline{)834}$

**11.** $978 \div 3$    **12.** $858 \div 2$    **13.** $595 \div 5$    **14.** $681 \div 3$    **15.** $872 \div 4$

_____    _____    _____    _____    _____

**16.** $784 \div 4$    **17.** $995 \div 5$    **18.** $642 \div 6$    **19.** $448 \div 4$    **20.** $609 \div 3$

_____    _____    _____    _____    _____

## Problem Solving • Reasoning

**21.** Susan bought a 575-piece jigsaw puzzle to put together. She invited four of her friends to help her. If they all place the same number of pieces into the puzzle, how many pieces would each person place?

_____

**22.** James is planning a trip to Washington, D.C. He lives 858 miles away. He has 2 days to drive there, and he wants to drive the same amount of miles each day. How many miles would he have to drive each day?

_____

Name _____  Date _____

# Divide Money

| Example |
|---|
| $3.19 |
| 2)$6.38 |
| − 6 |
| 03 |
| −2 |
| 18 |
| −18 |
| 0 |

**Divide.**

1. 4)$8.56  2. 3)$9.78  3. 6)$6.72  4. 5)$5.70

5. 5)$5.85  6. 3)$6.51  7. 2)$8.78  8. 4)$4.96  9. 8)$8.96

10. 3)$3.87  11. 2)$2.96  12. 4)$4.52  13. 6)$6.96  14. 3)$9.84

15. 3)$3.36  16. 2)$5.96  17. 4)$9.44  18. 5)$9.65  19. 2)$7.14

## Problem Solving • Reasoning

20. Julie went to the store to get some apples. They were on sale for $2.98 for 2 pounds. Julie bought 1 pound. How much did Julie pay?

_____

21. John got 4 paint brushes for $4.68. How much does 1 paint brush cost?

_____

Name _____   Date _____

# Placing the First Digit

| Example |
|---|
| 75 |
| 3)225 |
| − 21 |
| 15 |
| − 15 |
| 0 |

**Divide and check.**

**1.** 6)432     **2.** 8)592     **3.** 4)388     **4.** 2)154

**5.** 7)581     **6.** 5)340     **7.** 3)177     **8.** 2)116     **9.** 6)594

**10.** 8)392     **11.** 4)228     **12.** 9)558     **13.** 3)171     **14.** 7)392

**15.** 3)246     **16.** 5)355     **17.** 6)222     **18.** 7)182     **19.** 9)378

## Problem Solving • Reasoning

**20.** The swim team has to swim a total of 315 laps before the upcoming swim meet. They have 9 days left to practice. If they swim the same amount of laps each practice, how many laps would they have to swim each time?

_____

**21.** The baker at the corner bakery said that during the week of Thanksgiving, they bake as much as 679 loaves of bread. They work all 7 days of the week. How many loaves of bread do they bake per day if they bake the same amount of loaves each day?

_____

Name _____ Date _____

# Problem-Solving Application: Use Operations

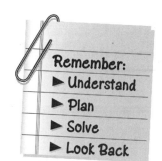

**Remember:**
► Understand
► Plan
► Solve
► Look Back

Sometimes when you solve a problem you need to decide which operations to use and in what order to use them.

**1.** Bob had 3 large boxes full of grapefruits and 1 box full of oranges. He had 1,100 pieces of fruit. If each box of grapefruits had 310 in it, how many oranges did Bob have?

**Think:** What operation can I use to solve this problem?

_____

**2.** Each week Jeff's family measures their height and weight. His dad weighs 4 times as much as Jeff. His dad weighs 236 pounds and his sister weighs 19 pounds less than Jeff. How much does Jeff's sister weigh?

**Think:** What operations do I need and in what order should I do them?

_____

**Solve. Use these or other strategies.**

---

**Problem-Solving Strategies**

• Draw a Picture  • Write a Number Sentence  • Make a Table

---

**3.** Mrs. Jones had 4 boxes of hardcover books and 1 box of paperback books to put on the shelves. She knew she had 940 books in all. If each box of hardcover books had 176 books in it, how many paperback books were there?

_____

**4.** Steve knew that the case of tomato cans weighs 2 times as much as the case of olives. The case of tomatoes weighs 86 pounds. The case of peppers weighs 7 pounds less than the olives. How much does the case of peppers weigh?

_____

**5.** Brian worked on his science project for 5 hours on Tuesday and Wednesday. He worked on it 7 hours on Saturday and 6 hours on Sunday. How many hours did he work on his project?

_____

**6.** Jane went to the store to buy school supplies. Markers cost $2.99 a pack and pencils were $1.50 a pack. How much will 3 packs of pencils and 2 packs of markers cost her?

_____